30ᵗʰ Annual Awards Issue

Making Tracks:

Escape or Journey

Nimrod International Journal

Awards 30

Nimrod International Journal IS INDEXED IN HUMANITIES INTERNATIONAL COMPLETE

The University of Tulsa is an equal opportunity/affirmative action institution. For EEO/AA information, contact the Office of Legal Compliance at (918) 631-2602; for disability accommodations, contact Dr. Jane Corso at (918) 631-2315.

ISBN: 0-9794967-2-1
Volume 52, Number 1

ISSN: 0029-053X
Fall/Winter 2008

THE UNIVERSITY OF TULSA
TULSA, OKLAHOMA

Acknowledgements

This issue of *Nimrod* is funded by donations, subscriptions, and sales. *Nimrod* and The University of Tulsa acknowledge with gratitude the many individuals and organizations that support *Nimrod*'s publication, annual prize, and outreach programs: *Nimrod*'s Advisory and Editorial Boards; and *Nimrod*'s Angels, Benefactors, Donors, and Patrons.

ANGEL ($1,000+)
Ellen Adelson, Margery Bird, Ivy & Joseph Dempsey, Marion & Bill Elson, Joan Flint, Edwynne & George Krumme, Susan & Robert Mase, Mary Lee Townsend & Burt Holmes, Rita Singer, Ann Daniel Stone, The John Steele Zink Foundation

BENEFACTOR ($500+)
William Bernhardt, Katherine & John Coyle, Cynthia Gustavson, Evelyn Hatfield, Bruce Kline, Robert LaFortune, Thomas Matson, Ruth K. Nelson, Donna O'Rourke & Tom Twomey, Marty Porreca, Leslie Ringold, Andrea Schlanger, Dorothy & Michael Tramontana, Randi Wightman, Jane Wiseman, Josephine & Thomas Winters

DONOR ($100+)
Harvey Blumenthal, Phil Bolian, Harry Cramton, Nancy & Ray Feldman, Sherri Goodall, Helen Jo Hardwick, Ellen Hartman, Frank Henke III, Ben Henneke, Nancy Hermann, Mary & Douglas Inhofe, Carol Johnson, James V. Jordan, Sam & Liz Joyner, Inge Kahn, The Kerr Foundation, William Kellough, Marjorie & David Kroll, Robert Lafortune, Sandra & Dobie Langenkamp, Maria Lyda, Roberta & Dan Marder, Geraldine McLoud, James McGill, Carol McGraw, James Millaway, Catherine Gammie Nielsen, Rita Newman, Oklahoma Visual Arts Coalition, Nancy & Tom Payne, Jeanine & H. E. Rainbolt, Lisa Ransom, Dana Rasure, Patricia Rohleder, R. A. Searcy, Joan Seay, Diane & James Seebass, Sarah Theobald-Hall, Fran & Bruce Tibbetts, Renata & Sven Treitel, Melissa & Mark Weiss, Marlene Wetzel, Joy Whitman, Penny Williams, Yevgeny Yevtushenko, Mary Young & Joseph Gierek

PATRON ($50+)
Margaret Audrain, Jean Curry, Ken Ferguson, Olivia Marino, John Mitchell, Bobbye Potter, Marjorie Singer, Maynard Ungerman, Maralee Waidner, Peter Waldor, Krista & John Waldron, Peter Walter, Ruth Weston, Martin Wing

TABLE OF CONTENTS

Making Tracks: Escape or Journey
Awards 30 and Conference 2008

Jal a drom, jal a drom (travel the road, travel the road), the Gypsies say. According to statistics, Americans are also a traveling lot. Despite failing finances and hard times, we make tracks seeking excitement, stimulation, and change—visual, visceral or imaginary. Often we are at the same time seeking escape from family, friends, homestead, and seeking answers to baffling yet fundamental questions. This is a partial interpretation of *Making Tracks: Escape or Journey*: the intentional quest or odyssey.

Along with the intentional odyssey is the search, quite often, for a guide willing to steer us through the labyrinthine course. Here is another goal of *Nimrod*'s theme for 2008: *Making Tracks: Escape or Journey*, to provide an opportunity to take an individual journey with leaders equal to Aeneas.

Each year, *Nimrod* goes the distance and brings expert guides to Tulsa to share their talents with registrants at the conference for readers and writers, to conduct workshops as well as to celebrate the winners of *Nimrod's* annual competition in fiction and poetry, and to congratulate the editors who, once again, have unflaggingly embarked on a journey of discovery, descended into a mountain of manuscripts, and emerged, eye-sore and spirit soaring—with winners.

The commitment and intentionality of our editors and writers are part of the process. Yet tracks are also made *un*intentionally. As the writers included in this issue are well aware, there are times when, starting out on flat land, we unintentionally trip and plunge into the unknown. We become lost in the deep, fish around until—awash in discovery—gasping for breath, we surface renewed, filled with vision, with story, with the knowledge that we have not only taken to the road, the river, or the ocean, but also experienced a *journey*. As Dostoyevsky's Dimitri tells us, "It is only from the depths we learn to sing the Ode to Joy." A journey is not just a trip (though we may trip several times along the way). It is not merely running away from but running the distance—no matter the emotional or physical pain demanded.

The entirety of this Awards Issue, *Making Tracks: Escape or Journey*, reflects the journey of the human mind and spirit in its quest to speak out and to speak well. The issue combines selections of poetry, fiction, and personal essays from the awards competition (there were 1279 submissions) and material accepted over the transom from submissions all during the year.

We begin our travels, in this 52nd year of publication and 30th year of giving awards, with the gypsies of Romania and then follow the migrants from Greece to the snow-covered plains of Wyoming in Paul Mihas's First Prize-winning story "This is Not a Barren Place," a story that begins with a hanging and ends with the vision of a boy, an angel, on a rooftop showering white snow on the black figures below. As our judge for 2008, Anthony Doerr, noted: "This writer displays the ability to transcend the world of the story."

Stephanie Soileau, author of "Camera Obscura" and Second Prize winner in fiction, initially sees its world through a pinhole and the focus is narrow and internal. As the inner journey progresses, the lens widens and the focal character moves beyond her fantasy world in a series of revelations that right her upside-down vision.

Responding to the wrenching division, dislocation, anger and grief of war, poems by First Prize-winner Elyse Fenton, and by four other authors (Peck, Hertzler, Weiss, and Simpson) track the minefields and emotional topography of Iraq, Afghanistan, Gaza, and Palestine and ultimately cry out in unison a "Tkhine" for peace and wholeness.

The issue travels from place to place in an exploration that is broad and trans-cultural as it probes the unknown. The pieces that emerge, as with any good archaeological dig, are mud-stained yet carry light. Ramanujam's story "Lions and Carnivals" set in India where theft and the caste system are still prevalent, is intrinsically tied to the golden boat of the Bengali poet, translated in this issue into Slovenian, French, and English, and Alexander's "Green Leaves" from Kerala.

The world trek also includes Aganga's Africa, Okere and Luce's Japan, Han-hua Chang's China, the Minnesota woods, the Oregon river, and the Oklahoma plains—gardens of loss and plenitude everywhere. For the journey and the escape are ultimately lived and remembered, sometimes with passion, sometimes in plainsong, and then breathing "a secret like the first bird waking," as in Jude Nutter's Second Prize poem.

Sarah Atlee, *Lawton Amarillo,* acrylic, ink and collage on canvas,
12" x 16"

from *Root Beggars*

Shuvani

Shu-shu-shu-Shuvani
>*Wise Woman*, we, the Gypsies, say.

Shoo-shoo-shoo Gitano
>*Go Away*, the gadje pray.
>Your words and stones may
>make us roam but the waxing
>moon will call us home

Jal a drom, jal a drom
>(travel the road, travel the road).

Remember

My mother's people say
        that by doing anything at all,
                we make ourselves vulnerable
to its opposite.   The word,
Meriben = life.   The word,
Meriben = death.   The words
are the same.   In a journey
of both shadow and sunshine
            of dark and light,
                of *kalo* and *loko*,
both are the same.   You may mistake
one for the other. But you must
remember   not to.   Try   not to.

I fear the words that I do not know,
yet they exist in another time. That I
will only know them in dreams, and they
will feel like tin on my tongue when I am awake.

I fear the words that I do know now,
but won't remember in the past and
in the future. I fear that my children
won't know how to remember or just
won't want to.

I fear the *kalo* of *Meriben*. I fear
        the *loko* of *Meriben*. I fear
                that I will mistake one
                        for the other.   That when it is time,
                                I will choose the *Meriben* wrapped
                                in a priest's cloak, while the crows,
                                        enclosed, peck away

                                at the lily through the heart.

Reading the Tarot: The Gypsy Migration Story and Butterflies, Copper

It's in my hands. They want to lift, pick the moon.
It's in the cards wrapped in red silk
embossed with gold flowers so thin light shows in.
It's in the cards, her side of the family out of Slovakia, my grandmother said,
trekking from her garden to sink to stove to table.
I was out under the porch building sand castles,
smells of cabbage soup, paprika, strudel
leaking through the screen door. I built roads and rivers.
I drew stars. I drew the seven of hearts with fluttering wings
on Lake Erie's shore.

Three five, the odd numbers falling out
of the 21 majors, uneven number
again, numerals sparking the dark like fireflies
I caught in a Kerr jar. Little golden chariots. I followed
their light until I let them go.
I could feel the dark in my veins. I tried
not to be afraid.

Women danced on the calendar my grandfather had nailed
to the cellar wall next to the coal bin, one
of the women dancing with her skirt and petticoats
billowing above her naked buttocks, her feet, arms,
face, all of her rising, spinning around ornamented
rhythms I breathed
into a spiral of fiery roses.
A flame, no body.

They were penny moons, silver-coined tambourines
I spanked and jangled in grade school. My wrist snapped

a path out of India to Egypt, listening
to the creaking wheels, wanting to see
some other side. As if the earth
was a coin to flip. Day, night "wheels within wheels."
Sun gone, the woman brought out a globe,
spread the cards and charged to see the other side.
Death, justice with pennies, and a magician
who lived in both worlds, who decided
what was real.

One push on the porch glider to Cleveland
and my aunt's corner grocery, oiled floors, sausage
behind the glass case, pickles, garlic. I could take
one licorice stick. Three pushes to Africa, four for China.
At night the train shook my metal bed, sparked
the tracks like hair-thin lightning tongues
a quarter-moon away. No matter Christ hung
framed above my bed, head encircled by a thorn crown,
his red heart quivering . . . I knew what the Queen
of Swords foretold: enter and leave alone.
She wore a butterfly crown and lace. The train whistled
itself to a ghost, I stopped shaking.

Fortune showed a powerful storm
in the full moon. No one can escape
the swords that fall when it's time. Ice covers the land,
mountains erupt. That's what the card says, she said, the teller
of the cards. No one can escape when it's their time
for misery, the swords blood-shined, the forces like an inferno.
See the red, she said. Forget you're afraid. Remember the garden crowned
with ripe tomatoes and what the road looked like under the moon, shape shifting
the clouds, weaving itself through the leafless trees.

Bees buzzed the ripened plums, their juice like resin.
Garden almost spent, my grandmother's kitchen steamed
with the canning, her knife coring, slicing, dicing for the jars.
He came once a year across the fields that stretched
every direction, house to house across Hungary, she said, with his pots
and pans clanking like a two-key band in the wagon, came each
year with his grinding wheel to sharpen the knives. He told stories,

she said, people who were good, people dancing with the devil
inside them. He told how his horse knew the road without stars or moon.
How the road was a river leading to its source,
to the telling of life in the faces of the cards. The Two of Pentacles
shaped an eight. Two snakes, one shedding its skin at the right time,
stars dying, hens birthing eggs for breakfast and for chicks
into hens into the Sunday dinner pot. Grandma used the hatchet,
then her knife like a sixth finger on her right hand for the rest.

I had to trust the driver who spoke no English to take me
to Osku, where the photograph from "the old country"
showed a family standing in the doorway, dark dresses,
baby with bonnet tied tight under her chin. They had one cow,
a few geese; they had so little, grandmother said, believing
in good, filling the boxes with donated hats, coats, and boxes of Kraft
macaroni and cheese. She'd lived with newspapers in her shoes
to outlast the cold winds that swept the fields
on her walk to school. An orange at Christmas, if they were lucky,
like a miracle. Each slice a sweet half-moon in the hoarfrost of winter.
This new country had bins and bins of oranges all year, so
who needed roads paved with gold, she said.

The geese honked and my driver pointed, made hand gestures
with a pretend fork from steering wheel to mouth.
Inside the cave, electric bulbs dangled over the scratched tables,
mismatched chairs, blue and white flowered china,
heavy forks and knives, the cave filled
with its molten heat and secret fissures, a womb out of the chaos
of lightning, breathing the breath of itself
and the smells of potato soup, chicken paprikash, and strudel.
My stomach glowed with the memory of it.
Her kitchen. My grandmother a four-foot-eight
queen of abundance. The memory of it, caves out of the beginning
of some birth, some time,
somewhere long back.

In a coffee house in Budapest, the smudged-face
girl sidled up to our table and put out her palm,
dirt-caked, fingernails bitten.

Her eyes glinted above her childlike smile. The waitress
shooed her away—but not before I put my uneaten pastry in her hand,
not before she looked down and spat,
before she disappeared like a thin penny
through the door.

In the town of Papa, relatives on my grandfather's side
said, eat, eat. The table bloomed with plates and dishes of food.
Drink the slivorice, the plum brandy, in one gulp for good luck,
for coming across the great ocean, drink, it is our habit.
Eat more goulash, more poppy seed horns. See
how your grandfather looks in this picture and you a baby
and your grandmother sent us pictures and how the whole village knew
when the boxes came and how we stood around
like it was an altar.

Drink and your grandfather's brother's grandson will continue
to translate. Look how we kept those years
and your grandfather who rode the great sea.
Those boxes your grandmother mailed smelled like America.
We wore the clothes, ate the food and we kept the pictures.
They shuffled the stack of black and white photographs
that showed part of the story. America, America,
the old man of the family whispered. America, he breathed.
Where we know now your roads are paved with rocks, his son
added, like our roads. But here you are, like a wish,
and your grandfather knows you have come.
So drink. Drink.

I studied The Fool who is without malice. He wore
a pouch filled with memories of the world.
He traveled over mountains under clear light.
He held a wand with the "head that looks
backward" to show past and present. He walked
without desire. So simple. I was the Copper Woman
dancing in my ancestors' fields of corn and sunflowers.
Butterflies circled their heads. I was the ore,
the conductor of glider swing to Cape Town,
Leningrad, Beijing, and Osku, still sitting
in the maple tree in my grandmother's yard

hidden on a branch among the large leaves humming
a little, waiting for a prince, for the next train,
my tongue clicking the clackety clack
of the wheels and making wishes.
Two licorice sticks next time. I was
Copper Woman fluttering and sparking
at the same time, my fingers snapping
the ornamented rhythms, mapping
the story, making me a funnel
of light on the river.

Sarah Atlee, *Peoria Jenks*, ink and collage on found fabric, 6" x 8"

from *Flesh Rose*

Green Leaves of El Fasher

Everything that's real turns to sun
Stones, trees, the jeeps they came in, those men.
In Jebel Marra, the leaves are very green.
Here, in El Fasher too.
I am singing, stones fill with music.
Do not touch my hair, I cried. They forced me
To uncover my head then beat me when my veil slipped,
Not the pink one I am wearing now, with stripes—this
My aunt gave me. I am not an animal,
They are more free, birds in the tree, horses too.
I am your language, do not cover me.
I am burning in what you take to be the present tense.
We are the letters *alif, ba, taa, mim*—
What the sun makes as it spins a nest of fire.

This Is Not a Barren Place

Nick Papadimitrios had hanged himself from a beam in his garage with a strand of baling wire. A garbage collector out of work, he had fallen into a depression, and, angry at the railroad workers who had thick wallets on Friday afternoon, he decided to find the cheapest way out of Rock Springs, Wyoming. Violeta, his wife, stared at him for no one knows how long and circled his suspended body—he wore straight-legged polyester pants—as if making sure he was really her man. She dragged a box of Pennzoil toward him, then climbed on top of it and began pulling at the wire. She whimpered, climbed down again, then ran to the kitchen. She grabbed the phone—it sat off the hook on the counter—and hung it up to get a dial tone. Her finger circled around the numbers that located the voice of Helen Yanopolous, the first Greek woman she had met when she had stepped off the train seven years ago. Violeta, speaking only in Greek, cried through garbled words. Helen promised she'd be right over, and Violeta, with clammy hands, slipped the receiver back in its place.

In the garage, with a steak knife, she sawed at the wire. Then she grabbed the wire clippers hanging from a cup hook by the light switch and snipped it her first try. He thudded to the cement, bones cracking when he hit. She gasped, then stepped down from the box and knelt beside him. She put her hand on his chest and, blinking, listened for breath. For the longest time, she stood guard at the door to the kitchen and made sure no one would walk in. No noise then but the sound of a doorbell ringing and knocking. She slipped out of the garage and hurried across the living room to the front door. She opened it. Helen, purse in hand, stood waiting.

Violeta breathed through her mouth, pressed her fingers against her forehead. Helen tilted her head, tried to read Violeta's face. Then the widow grabbed Helen's hand and walked her to the garage as if it she were about to show her an iceberg or a meteor shower. From outside Helen heard the squeals and laughter of Violeta's two girls, neither in school yet. In the garage the two women looked at each other, and, without words, asked each other which one should stay with the body and which one should serve chocolate chip ice cream on the patio. Helen pushed Violeta toward the yard.

"Take care of them," Helen said.

Violeta, her face white, her hair teased into a puff hairdo, wiped dust and tears from her eyes and opened the door to the backyard as Helen began covering the body with a plastic tablecloth. She emptied out Nick's pockets—two quarters and a drink stirrer—and began an inventory from the neck down, urine trailing across the floor, his final signature, the most legible word his body had ever written.

❀ ❀ ❀

On the day before the funeral Violeta put black dye in a tub of warm water and dyed all her clothes black, the green skirts and the navy blue socks and red blouses. Later, she sorted a pile of black on the couch in the living room, frowned at the buttons that had turned to gray. Her girls played the same record over and over again and sat fixated on the album cover. They were doing what little girls do, dreaming of little stories to blow into myths. As Violeta gathered loose socks from the laundry, a toy telescope dropped from the couch cushion to the floor. Inside it you could pretend to see the whole universe, the bottom of a drain.

❀ ❀ ❀

After the funeral, in her kitchen, Helen covered the mashed potatoes and wiped the gravy boat with a washcloth. Her sixteen-year-old son, Tony, wrapped his skinny body in the phone cord as he complained about his latest English quiz. He had refused to go to the church and looked as if he had spent the whole day on the phone. Helen's husband, George, at the kitchen table, lifted his head from the obituaries. His curly hair was still slick from the gel.

"What kind of man does that? Hangs himself in his own house?"

"A man in exile," she said in Greek.

"Two kids," George said.

"I put together a box of Tony's old Match Box cars for them."

"You gave away my suit."

"It made you look fat."

"Do you know what it's like, watching a dead man wear your suit? In a coffin? Couldn't they put him in some pajamas?"

"Stop it."

"He was going to be buried."

"You don't feel sorry for her?"

"He couldn't hold a job. I already felt sorry for her."

❈ ❈ ❈

When George drove off in the Pontiac at 10 p.m. to begin his graveyard shift at the railroad, Helen stood in the doorway of Tony's bedroom.

"If you are ever sad, talk to me," she said.

"Okay." He stared at his feet.

"Don't try to hurt yourself."

"Okay."

"Do you want to know a secret?"

"Yes."

"Suicide is contagious, and Greek men are like dominoes. I'm afraid who's next."

In bed, alone, she thought of the many ways Nick could have killed himself. Driving the car off the Rock Springs cliff. Slipping into the hot lava at Yellowstone. Bleeding from slashed wrists in the laundry room. A body was a difficult thing to end. Sometimes she fell asleep with Nick drowning himself at Flaming Gorge and by morning he was in the garage again, this time suffocated by carbon monoxide, Charlie Pride on the radio. Sometimes there were gunshots; sometimes only pills.

The next day when her husband slept through game shows to recover from the night shift, she drove to Violeta's house, even though it was only three blocks away. The garage door was open, Violeta sweeping the cement floor. She wore a black blouse and a black skirt, black hose and flat, black shoes. Helen wished she could undo it all, undye the clothes, unhang the hanging man, undo the knot in the wire, but it was as impossible as unbaking Easter bread.

"How much longer will you wear black?" Helen said.

Violeta swept at strands of hair and dragged the broom over the blood that wasn't there. "Forever."

Helen wandered to the Buick in the driveway, opened the car door, called to the girls, who slipped into the daylight. They wore black dresses and black socks that went up to their knees.

"Let's go for a drive." She motioned to Violeta. "You, too."

Helen drove them around the block, then past the Shell station by the railroad. Violeta surveyed the miles of dirt and sagebrush that stretched on either side of them. Helen got on the highway and kept driving past Little America, the gas station with the Disney figures, and drove all the way to Flaming Gorge.

They drove along a stretch of weeds and parked near the water. The surface of the lake seemed lavender under the cloud, an explosion of white, across the lake. The girls bolted from the car, ran to the shore, scattering pebbles as they raced to find shells. Helen undid her shirt, then finally removed it entirely, letting the sun pour over her. The sun sank onto her skin and white bra. Violeta unbottoned her blouse.

"I'm never out in the sun."

"The sun is for children," Helen sat on the hood, then scooted up farther and laid her head on the windshield. Violeta sat with her arms folded across her half-opened blouse.

"I wonder if he would have done it if he had married you instead." Violeta's eyes stayed on the girls.

"He would have done it married to Marilyn Monroe."

In the sunlight her blouse looked deep purple. Black dye didn't cover everything.

"The neighbors are going to wonder where I've been."

"Even Persephone got to leave every now and again."

❊ ❊ ❊

Hours later, after dropping off the widow and girls, Helen drove the car into the gravel driveway of her house as if she were rowing a destroyer. The headlights landed on George, who seemed to be pacing inside the enclosed porch. He put his hand against his forehead, transfixed, like a guilty man in a Hitchcock movie.

He looked as if he were searching for his wallet, feeling his ribs beneath his powder-blue shirt. She didn't say anything, but it was like seeing Nick again, out of work with nothing to do but catalog cracks on the ceiling or stare at a stain on his shirt sleeve.

She opened the car door, felt the last bit of light in the sky.

"Did someone else hang himself?" he said.

"We fell asleep in the sun."

He grabbed the keys from her fist. He looked at her arms, up and down her solid body. "Do you think I'm too hard on you?"

"What do you think?" Helen poked at the skin of her sunburned neck.

"You smell like lotion."

"You smell like coal."

Inside, she filled him in on the day, on the growing creases on Violeta's forehead.

"She says she's going to wear black forever."

"Our own Johnny Cash." He started singing "Ring of Fire."

Tony walked through the kitchen, fringed jeans sweeping the linoleum, and ignored her. He grabbed the phone off the wall. Last year he had fallen in love with a foreign-exchange student named Anneliese, who had left in June for Sweden. Helen remembered that girl as everything she had never been, lean with white-blonde hair and eyes the color of the water in a swimming pool.

"You're not calling her, are you?" Helen asked.

"I wish." He stared back at her and pulled the cord as far as it would go into the porch, dark now that the sun had almost set, till his voice sounded like someone trapped in a barrel.

"He's been making crank phone calls again." George's eyes glinted.

"What?"

"He called the Vatican. In Rome."

"How did he get *that* number?"

"How should I know?"

"What did they say?"

"Whoever answered said to call back during regular business hours."

"Tony!" she called out.

On the porch, he sank to the floor and kept his conversation going.

"He's probably tracking down the number for the White House."

"He's going to embarrass us."

"Men are hanging themselves left and right, and he's calling the goddamn Pope. Father Dimitri is going to take away his altar boy robe."

"He was planning to use that for Halloween."

"Who was he going to be? The Pope?"

❉ ❉ ❉

They lived on different pages of the calendar. For Tony it was almost Halloween. For Helen, almost Thanksgiving. For George, almost Christmas. It was something they couldn't name. It was the obituary page on every kitchen table in every single-story house on Elk Avenue, but not in Violeta's house. There, it was almost New Year's—no, after New Year's—and the half-bottle of Metaxa brandy Nick had drunk the morning he died was still sitting on the counter. It was George belting out a Johnny Cash song, "Cry Cry Cry." Leave the little widow alone. Let her pour her own memories down the sink. It was short mornings that started whenever George got up at two or three or four a.m. for whichever shift he had that day that lasted eight hours or ten hours or twelve hours depending on which other shift the other guys had and whichever shift he had just had the night before or the day before or the full moon before. It was Helen washing her hair in the kitchen sink while Tony, locked in their only bathroom, feathered his hair in silence. It was calling Violeta—Leta they called her now—back to life, to Wyoming, for a close look at the daughters who were waiting for her to answer questions like "will you marry again?" while the rest of them watched her battered face, beat-up from too much sleep on those rough couch pillows, grown old in just a matter of weeks. No, it was just days. Helen could have sworn those lines, those half-shadows, had not been there before the hanging. Whatever it was had crept into Tony, too. She found him dialing random numbers at odd hours and ordering sausage pizza for folks at some other address on Elk Avenue. This craziness hadn't been there before the hanging. He hated sausage.

❉ ❉ ❉

George, in pajamas, was waving at her under the awning of their house. He had a drink in his hand and held it as if he was Cary Grant. "Get the hell over here."

Back from her latest trip to Violeta's, she sat down on the steps of the front stoop.

"I don't know how to tell you this," he said. "He just called the Kremlin."

She looked up. "What?"

"He probably got the CIA on our backs."

"Did he hang up right away?"

"He kept some guy on the line." He was watching her intently now.

"I can't believe it." She shook her head.

"Every time you look away, this crap happens."

"Don't start blaming me."

"Then I cut the phone cord."

"What?"

"To teach him a lesson. He wouldn't hang up."

The storm door creaked open and Tony stepped out.

"I don't want to live here. People kill themselves here."

"Don't say that," Helen said.

"They drag a knife up the sternum and take out your insides and pump you full of formaldehyde. You don't even get to keep your liver."

"What?" George said.

"After you die!" Tony was almost screaming.

"He's having trouble in English," George said. "Composition."

Tony lifted his head at the sky, clouds rolling in. "Maybe we're already dead. We're just the particles and stuff that's left over."

Helen gave her son a look of yearning. "Let me fix you a milkshake."

"His teacher said he can't figure out what a topic sentence is," George said.

"Topic sentences are fascist."

"Are they now?" George sloshed around the half-melted ice cubes in his glass.

"I need to figure things out."

"You do that, sonny boy."

Tony let go of the door, and it banged shut.

"What are we going to do?" Helen rubbed her palm. "Everything's different now."

"Fix another drink."

"You already have a drink." She stared at his glass.

"Highballs are like eyeballs. One is not enough."

Helen looked up at the door. "I blame that albino girl."

"They say it might snow." He stood up.

"That's perfect. I'm going to stay inside and bake. The church is going to have a bake sale for widows," she said in Greek.

"For the love of God," he said. "What about guys who donated their suits to deadbeats. What are we supposed to eat?"

❖ ❖ ❖

Later, as Helen rolled out the dough for the *kouloria*, she noticed the light glowing from the gas oven. She thought about how Tony could just stick his head in there when no one was around and that would be the end of it. Then, peering out the lace curtain, she saw the snow hitting the windowpane. She picked up the phone, with the cord dangling off the table, and, out of habit, hung it back on the receiver. The wind crackled through the aluminum siding. After she put the *kouloria* in the oven, she sat with arms folded on the couch. Through lace curtains horizontal snow moved toward her like a plane of stars, as if the house itself were flying through space. She could see it all. Snow covered the hoods of cars at the dealership across the street. Wind tunneled through alleyways and warehouses. Flags whipped around poles. Reed grass stuck out sideways, hubcaps rolled across parking lots. Bluejays and twigs hit against windowpanes. Hound dogs yelped.

On the television screen, a brunette in an old movie winked at her lover as if she could tell the future. The smoke from her cigarette corkscrewed its way to the top of the screen. Women in movies either knew nothing, staring blankly at the horizon, or understood too much, like women from the ancient tragedies who could trick you under your own roof. Helen fell asleep to the sound of gunshots and sirens from the black and white screen. Outside, more snow.

In the morning, she turned off the television and wandered to the kitchen. She grabbed the phone, forgetting about the severed cord, and heard nothing, no sound. She put on her coat, scarf and boots, opened the front door, and, eyes half-closed, stood in front of the storm door. Snow reached up to the window. She gasped, closed the door, then retreated to the kitchen, where, still wearing her coat, she nibbled on a *koulori*. She checked on Tony, still asleep, his pillow folded around his head. When he was a child, before kindergarten, she would read to him, or pretend to, though she didn't know English. Every time she turned the pages of *Winnie the Pooh*, it would have a different ending. Sometime Pooh would end up in Russia, or in Copenhagen, drinking honey with the Little Mermaid or running between columns at the Temple of Poseidon. Tony had come to believe that words in books magically shifted once you closed the cover. She was the one who had persuaded him to shut his eyes so that she could take him to the top of the Taj Mahal and the steps of the Parthenon. And she did. When he had started school he was disappointed to see that words in books were nailed down, immovable, boring. He asked her to read Dick and Jane for him, to see if those kids could do anything besides feed their dog. But she had put away her mystical carpet and left him with nothing but words and pictures that never changed. It's no wonder he had trouble with English. "I'm sorry," she said.

He rolled over and took the pillow from his head. He saw her standing there, and his eyes filled with tears.

"Honey, what's wrong?" she said.

He ran his fingers down the bridge of his nose, cleared his eyes.

"I'm not going away till you say something."

He grunted.

"Say something."

"Something."

"I'm waiting."

Tony rubbed a pimple on his chin. "He talked to me."

"Who?"

"Nick."

"He's dead."

"When he was alive. He called. Here."

"What do you mean?"

"I could tell he was messed up. He wanted someone to go over there and find him, so that she wouldn't have to find him."

Helen swallowed, examined her son's face.

"He was planning it, Mom."

Helen stared at him, then at the drapes.

"It should have been me, not you," he said. "Who went over there." He got out of bed. He was wearing his jeans and t-shirt from yesterday. He put on his boots, grabbed his vinyl coat from the floor.

"What are you doing? There's no place to go," Helen said. "Look." She moved toward the far wall, pulled open the drapes. Sun poured through the white snowdrift. The crenulated edge of the drift reached almost to the top of the picture window. Icicles hung from the roof outside.

Tony, squinting, stood transfixed before the flood of shimmer and light, letting it fill his vision, as if he were standing before an army of angels, a story she might have told him as a child. The magic carpet had returned for him.

"Goddamn."

"Why didn't you come to me?"

"She was supposed to call," he said.

"She?"

"Anneliese! But I picked up the phone, and it was him. Telling me how he was going to do it and everything. Wire. Baling wire. Motherfucker."

He climbed onto the bed and looked out the side window. He opened it, unhooked the screen.

In moments he had tricked his way into the opening and onto the mound of snow just outside it.

"Don't go out there."

"This is like six feet of snow."

She got on the bed and stuck her head out the window. "Tony!"

She zipped up her coat, dug for the gloves in the pockets, then crawled out the window. She eased herself down, her heels sinking into a foot of snow. The crisp air bit into her skin. Whoever said this was not a barren land was probably frozen beneath six feet of white bleakness, below her feet, next to the buried petunias. She surveyed the world around her. Snow had found its way into creek beds and ditches, into bird feeders, over stacks of firewood, and across railroad tracks, but she began trudging through the valley of the drift where the snow was only a foot deep. The drifts had stolen bicycles from their spots along sheds, slouched across horizontal single-wide trailers, and buried antennas that no repairman would ever touch. A bird flew across the dealership. A bare tree stood motionless. After suicide, there was still weather. Her eyes settled on Tony, who was working his way across a valley between rows of houses as if invisible sled dogs were pulling him forward.

"Jesus Christ," George's head was sticking out the window.

"He's running away," she said.

"Well, tell him not to."

If he had been a man in a movie, George too would be found hanging from a rope in the garage, but here, now, he was just her man, someone who could not let her go because he needed his eggs scrambled and couldn't find a fork. He couldn't tie a knot if his afterlife depended on it. She wrapped the scarf around her head and headed toward her son. Breath smoked out of her body as she stepped over a bird carcass. The world, never whiter, was frozen. The light of the white sky, veiled in clouds, pounded her eyes. She marched onward. George's voice seemed farther and farther away against the crunch of snow. She forgot where she was and where she was going. She forgot the names of neighbors she passed. She forgot the face of Violeta's dead husband. Her mind was occupied now only by this white desert, which seemed to spread farther with every step she took. She tiptoed around a spot where the frozen ground, uncharged by humanity, glimmered with water and ice. Before her, Tony trudged across the white plain that had slipped across roofs and alleys, as if he were Dr. Zhivago looking for sled dogs to take him to his lover. He was doing what immigrants used to do, making a way out of this cold white heaven, lifting their heads on occasion to see what the sky would bring. Behind them, Greeks left a trail of bodies, golden-skinned children they once were, mothers who longed for them, first loves who disappeared into marriages with others. She passed houses with ripped awnings, heard babies crying inside two-bedroom houses half-buried in the great drift. Terriers, trapped inside living rooms, barked. Somewhere, she couldn't even tell which direction, she heard a shovel hitting cement and the sound of men swearing.

Then, in the distance, the top half of the house with the red fiberglass awning floated into view. She saw him there, on the slanted roof, his arms spread, inching his way to the peak. She caught her breath, felt the cold in her toes, and plodded forward.

When she was close enough, she called to him. He was on his

back now, flapping his arms, making the top half of a snow angel. Breath plumed out of his body.

"Stay there. We'll get you down. Don't you dare move."

"I'm going to tell her!"

"Don't move." She sank to her knees and started to cry, then crawled onto the snow drift that edged to the picture window of the living room. She peeked in and saw them there, two girls jumping up and down, like children caught in a snow globe, their collars flopping as they jumped. She knocked on the window, and Violeta moved closer to the glass, looked up at her with eyes blank and unblinking. Her once-famous youth had vanished, eroded by what sheepherders still called the wild west. Helen tried to wipe tears with her gloved hands. She wanted to tell Violeta that on her roof a boy was flailing his wings, summoning her dead husband, that the cold white would turn into creek water, that school buses would rise from the world's frozen crawl space. After too many days of black dresses and bloodshot eyes, through the double-paned window, just inches from her now, Violeta cracked a smile. She was like a woman in a movie, and she already knew all this.

The Closed Mouth Fish

El pez de la boca cerada

I

My mother sought darkness
to learn of grave things.

She'd pause to consider a whisper
from an empty socket
of a fallen hibiscus or murmurs
from a surrendering ocean wave.

She listened for secrets dropped
in furrows along side streets, sneaking
underneath homes, in between
gangways of *compañeros*

to learn when she could visit my father again
at *El Castillo de Príncipe*, a prisoner
condemned to thirty years. Waiting
for my mother to emerge, also

a *gusano:* tired of standing in lines
to eat, refusing to wash away
shades of Africa from her skin,
rejecting demure tones to speak: *comrades*.

But no rumors crept into her open ears
nor sickle sounds seethed from Castro's
radio hosts announcing *su permiso*.

II

Days passed into shallow shapes
of moons, absent my father's face,
month after month: weariness.

She wanted to see him in uniform
or cast in gray. To see his chest
move up and down as he strangled
his own rage, waiting.

She needed to spin raw silk
from the ducts of her eyes and coil
it around a reel, string it to a rod,
at the end: lure, laced with *miel*.

Waiting, she prayed for him
on her knees, her back, her feet
until her blood turned blue like Yemayá,
goddess of the sea, mother of fish.

My mother waited to lift from sleep
and hear the murmur of an angel
hum and sigh and hum again, carnival rhymes:
this gift she must bring to the Orisha,

Yoruba saints, gods of all things.
Not coconuts, nor candles,
nor crow's feet. No more spinning silk
tangling rays of sight. Simply,

a closed mouth fish, which swallowed
my father's name whole, thick with honey,
nailed to her front door and hidden
from a scalding sun. Waiting months

for my father's release, for the angel to speak:
Espera, mi querida, tres días mas
for the fish mouth to open,
for his name to escape, and on that day

préparate, prepare to travel a protesting sea.

Greening the Blast Zone

(Mount St. Helens, Washington, erupted May 18, 1980)

After the blast
seared every living thing, scythed off
Mount St. Helens at the top, left a lop-sided
curiosity, regal-boned beneath scars,
and a blizzard of ash —

Lupine
took hold. Within five years, how the plant waved
wild-headed spikes and never tired.

My mother never tired.
She knew how to make the best of things,
adjusting, without rancor, to cancer's
raw orange sphere, the fiery core of haywire
tissues expanding in her left breast.

I still hear her voice,
like bells, as the New England wind
gnawed at our quickening steps
in her garden. The ash pit brought her joy
where some rampant parsley kept on.

Touching the green a poppy left behind
that held the memory of blood,
Mama told me a fable:
Once a woman, finding her clothes gone,
swept from her line by wind,
unpinned the light,
folded it voluminous in her basket. She shook out

droplets from her hands
that smelled clean as new roots.

       Fine for a fable.
Truth is, lodgepole pine moved back in;
shoved lupine out.
Some courage, I suppose, made Mama spare me
what grew in her like blight.
      I came away with her kindness,
a greening in me
taking hold over and over.

Rose Hip, from the collection of the Editor

The Visionary

after Ernst Barlach, relief,
Hamburg Memorial, *1931*

A woman in profile looking
not at us but to the future,
her daughter's head against
her breast. Their dresses
press together, and they wear
no shoes. There is nowhere to go.

What she sees now
isn't the hunger of the first war,
women in line for bread while
husbands, fathers fight in the trenches.

She sees bombs that will fall
on Hamburg. Streets and canals
on fire, people who've fallen asleep
from the fumes, others stumbling
over charred corpses, and there's
that boy in the distance behind
his mother whose clothes
have caught fire. He's smothering
the flames with his hands.

Infidelity

When you were in Iraq I dreamed you
dead, dormant, shanked stone

in a winter well, verb-less object
sunk haft-deep through the navel

of each waking sentence. I dreamed
myself shipwreck, rent timbers

on a tidal bed, woke to morning's cold
mast of breath canted wide as a searchlight

for the drowned. Dreamed my crumbling
teeth bloomed shrapnel'd bone light

bricks mortared into a broken
kingdom of sleep where I found you

dream-sift, rubbled, nowhere.
Forgive me, love, this last

infidelity: I never dreamed you whole.

Refusing Beatrice

Dante needed a whole committee —
Beatrice, Lucy, Virgil — to guide him
> down and back, even though hell

was a known descent, a matter of pages, a book
ending in certainty with a hero seeing stars.

> You've got no itinerary. Just an armored car
> > to ferry you down the graveled airport road, a Chinook

> > gut-deep in the green swill waiting to dislodge.

Maybe it's time to stop comparing —
I could never be Beatrice, couldn't harbor such good faith.

> And I won't be there in the Tigris basin to watch
> > heat flake cinders of paint from the Chinook's body
> > > like a rug shook out

> or see it hasten to the sky's surface
> > > like an untethered corpse —

My curse or gift is blindness;
> > I've never read this story before.

> And if the updraft's whirlwind
> > doesn't make the sniper miss, if your helicopter lifts

> > > from Baghdad as doomed as the Chaldean sun,

> I won't be there to see the wreckage
> > or papery flames, the falling arsenal of stars —

Your Plane Arrives from Iraq for the Last Time

> Through a round aperture I saw appear
> Some of the beautiful things that Heaven bears,
> Where we came forth, and once more saw the stars.
> —*Dante*, The Inferno, *Canto XXXIV*

Texas overcast. The road toward post
needle-pricked in brake lights, start-
and-stop of the heart's four chambers

involuntarily bound. And once more
the sky's feathered jet-stream, and once
more, the dirge and caesura of rotors

and once more the slow Morse of the plane's
body descending. And at the end
of the longest sentence I've ever known

your face in the window's fogged aperture:
stranded noun, Rorschach of stars. *Beautiful thing.*

Clamor

Staking fencing along the border of the spring
garden I want suddenly to say something about
this word that means sound and soundlessness
at once. The deafening metal of my hammer strikes
wood, a tuning fork tuning my ears to a register
I'm too deaf to understand. Across the yard

each petal dithers from the far pear one white
cheek at a time like one blade of snow into
the next until the yard looks like the sound
of a television screen tuned last night to late-
night static. White as a page or a field where
I often go to find the promise of evidence of you

or your unit's safe return. But instead of foot-
prints in the frosted static there's only late-
turned-early news and the newest image of a war
that can't be finished or won. And because last
night I turned away from the television's promise
of you I'm still away. I've staked myself

deep to the unrung ground, hammer humming
in my hand, the screen's aborted stop-time still
turning over in my head: a white twist of rag
pinned in the bloody center of a civilian's chest,
a sign we know just enough to know it means
surrender, there in the place a falling petal's heart would be.

365 and a Wakeup

DEROS: Date Eligible for Return from Overseas,
or Date of *Expected* Return, or *Estimated* Return,
opinions varied, but everyone in the Army counted
days: one year after arrival in-country, time to go
back to the World. Harrison said DEROS stood for
Don't Ever Rely on Sergeants, or Doubt Every
Rationale Offered by Superiors. Harper thought
that Double Each Round of Scotch sounded better,
but he was a lifer and a drunk. Billy Thorpe, after
a childhood of John Wayne movies, favored Destroy,
Eliminate, Ravage or Slaughter, and Samuels, that
egghead, suggested Deleterious Education in Reality
Offered Students Otherwise Recreating Endlessly
in Denial, but no one had a clue as to what that meant,
and what the hell is a palindrome, anyway? Most of us
just kept calendars—in pockets or rucksacks, drawn
on helmets or, in one case, scratched on the stock
of a rifle, crossing out the days, one by one, until you
were *short*, closing in on your DEROS: *I'm so short,*
I need a ladder to put on my boots. I'm so short, I could
parachute off a dime, so short I can walk under a snake
with my hat on. Some soldiers felt invincible: survived
this long, what's another few weeks? Others grew
paranoid, wouldn't change socks, carried extra ammo,
wore their flak jackets even when they slept. 365 and a
wakeup—unless you chose to voluntarily extend your
time in-country. *I love killing dinks*, Sgt. Villers confided
to me when he heard I'd extended my tour. *I'm staying*
longer too. And when I said I'd done so to receive
a six-month early out and return home a civilian, he
said *oh* and *well*, then walked away.

Tkhine in Sh'vat

The renewal of the moon shall be for you a
beginning of new moons; it shall be for you the
first among the months of the year.
—*Exodus 12:2*

Lord, if you're out there today
hesitating someplace between the branches of trees
in the interstices of black matter,
or in the dotted lines that stitch
hemispheres into a radiant globe,

I, your daughter, beseech you
who reflects
from beneath the cool shadow
of her parents' death
so I may

take a breath and exhale
into a lover's ear
as you score
chronicles of the winding canal,
through and out

listening so closely, you may understand
the sorrows of the world, and by that
I don't mean the common everyday stubbing,
but why a child is shot in the abdomen
by a stray bullet, while taking piano lessons,

glass shattering,
or how a journalist is gunned down in the street

for telling truth, in my own community,
far from other cities where terrible things happen
for which I have no ample words.

All I know
is I must find my way back to you
like a child
pushing through wild grass
wandering far from home.

Johanna Burton, *Surveying*, intaglio print

Tkhine in Adar

What Is Revealed / What Is Hidden

1.
Last night I heard frogs
that survived the winter in Leona Canyon
celebrating their mutual existence
a chorus of peeps and croaks
from beneath piled reeds.

2.
More hidden is Gaza
where wounds are always open
shipments of medical supplies
and food pour through barricades
from beneath the watchful eye of the Sphinx
while children sell their bodies
wondering where on standby
God waits and at which airport.

3.
A cantor sings Saturday morning
of the dwelling place for the *mishkan*
where the *Shekhinah* builds her nest
from our offerings, twisted linen
blue, purple and crimson
yarns with a design of two cherubim,
a breathing space for Your holy spirit
to huddle between.

4.
Help me this morning to understand
why countries can only offer
law and not justice,
why peace
is the absence of war,
why hate
sings Your name,
and why our hands clutch
at these gold nuggets of fear.

Tkhine in Adar II

I come before you,
a woman who catches white blossoms
before they drift to the ground,

begging you, merciful God,
to allow my country to hear the words
of the Winter Soldiers
testifying this weekend in Washington, D.C.,
how they can no longer
honor military guidelines for killing
other human beings,
and while I'm on the subject,

allow the people of Israel and Palestine
to become so weary of violence
they demand of their leaders
to find an olive branch
which has not been cut down,
and to stand beneath its small shade
as they approach each other
with an offering of fresh goat's milk.

Shrapnel

Last week I heard that a guy I used to work
with at a record store was killed somewhere

in the Anbar province (Arabic meaning "ware
house") when an I.E.D. dismantled his right leg.

The portrait of his face as I remember it haunts me,
and I often wonder if he died instantly or several days

later as his body turned pale and septic, while school
buses back home were busy loading children

from the sidewalks and sprinklers watered the great
lawns of suburbia. Already the morning is humid

and full of bird song, but I don't want to think *song*
or *lullaby*. The absence of sound is a blade that cuts

closer to bone until the world is reduced to its basic
intentions—hunger and parallel lines, death and disease.

A woman I once knew told me she loved the smell
of silage and the patchwork canvas of Holsteins

on her father's farm. She said as a young girl her body
would disappear into the shrill droning of cicadas

at dusk. It was not the sound itself she loved,
but the bitter appetite, the suicidal lust for oblivion

that echoed from pecan trees along the creek.
Their call filled the spaces of her body,

and as summer changed into autumn, she swore
she could hear them dying. The airless morning

swells after weeks without rain. It is something,
I think, to be entirely occupied with the living.

Miami, OK

I can do whatever I want. I'm rich, I'm famous, and I'm
bigger than you.
—*Don Johnson*

My parents' bedroom, 1987, gateway to the land
of Technicolor and remote controls, where every Thursday
night that electric opening fueled by stereophonic guitars
and Afro-Caribbean drums would echo through the house,
signaling the beginning of *Miami Vice*—wild flamingos
and busty women, sweeping helicopter shots of the great
Atlantic surf crashing into South Beach. How could you
not love the barely plausible exploits of Crockett & Tubbs
as they operated undercover, driving Ferraris and go-fast boats
and wooing all those cocoa-butter damsels in distress?
How could you not love the slip-on, sockless loafers,
white linen pants, Armani jackets, t-shirts in shades of pink,
blue, green, and fuchsia, the big-ass Ray-Bans and Floridian
sunsets falling behind the buildings of downtown Miami?
My mother loved Don Johnson the way girls once loved
the Beatles or Elvis, and she often joked she'd leave my father
in a heartbeat for her Don Juan of the Everglades with his
rugged good looks, tan skin, and slick hair, leaving me
and my younger brother to feel sorry for a Scots-Irish
lineman with a cleft chin and a bad temper. The poor bastard
wouldn't stand a chance, we thought, should fate intercede,
and, late at night, listening to our parents have sex from our
twin bunk beds, giggling at the asthmatic breathing and muffled
moans that sometimes sounded like pain, I'd picture
his ghost-image lingering on the screen, all beard stubble
and white teeth, watching them make love in the dark.
How could you blame her for the fantasy of a glamorous cop
busting drug lords and pimps and saving her from the hopelessness
of Oklahoma and Reagan's trickle-down depression,
for her resistance to a place whose beauty lies in wheat fields
and oil fields and cattle fields and barren fields where nothing
but mesquite trees grow, whose beaches surround muddy lakes
that will stain a white bathing suit faster than you can say bleach?

And how can you blame me for taking after my mother,
that bodily ache for things I can't possess — muscle cars and Super
Bowl tickets, Jennifer Beals dancing around my living room
in her *Flashdance* leotard? After all, there's an "I" in *family*
and another in *vice*, though it rides between two consonants
the way I'm sliding, years later, between the land of the living
and the kingdom of desire. Even now, as I stand in my bedroom
holding a honeymoon photo of me and my wife on a beach
in Cozumel, two lowercase i's wading in the surf beneath blue
skies, I'm thinking of someone else, a different wife, a better wife
standing with me on a better beach closer to Miami.

Jordan Haldane, photograph

The Camera Obscura

It's the most embarrassing things that get you: how he pours salt into his hand before sprinkling it pinch by pinch onto his asparagus; the way he looks up over his glasses with eyebrows arched and magnified eyes startled that the world is in fact right-side-up; the green button-down shirt with the cuffs rolled to the elbows and the unflattering jeans and the thick white socks and the white rubber gardening shoes, none of which have been changed in the three days since you started to notice him at all and maybe longer; and the way he catches you watching him pinch salt onto his asparagus and blinks giant eyes at you with purpose, with resolve, because you did something like this two days ago when you noticed him watching you deliver your lunch tray to the dish cart, and he's caught on, and this is flirting, and he's going to give it a whirl. Not to mention, of course, certain pertinent details of your own personal life, namely, that you are, as of a year ago and admittedly with some lack of enthusiasm—yes, in hindsight it seems like a grave mistake but, at the time, how *had* you felt at the time?—married.

He lingers at the lunchroom table with no food or drink in front of him, and you realize of course that you've communicated your interest a little too clearly and he's lingering just for you, and after he's finally given up and left, your fellow teachers at the table say with revulsion (and with some affection, too) that he seems so "out of phase." What do you do when this ticklish absurdity masquerades as persistent, budding joy? What do you do?

You wander casually into his photography studio as you and the other teachers have been invited to do, to come and enjoy the camera obscura that he's made of the room, lens boxes in every boarded-up window and bedsheet partitions catching the light and colors like butterflies in a net. The outside is inside: shadowy, silent, upside down.

It makes unfamiliar what is familiar, but for you, who are new to this high school, this town, called away from a life in a city a thousand miles away, where you had spent the last decade content with the limits of your map, for you, in this room, this new place is doubly strange. It is dizzying, this disorientation.

So you push aside a bedsheet and step through a shaft of projected light that contains in its colors the orange of a school bus, the gray-green of late summer grass, the fish-school fluttering of students dismissed. The photographer is leaning there, arms crossed like a museum guard.

You pester him with inane questions, growing bolder and clumsier by the minute. You ask how it works, the camera obscura. You ask him to show you his lens. You ask why the leaves seem to move so slowly, why the room feels so still, and you ask this unrelated thing that you've always wondered and been too embarrassed to ask — and he seems like the kind of man who would know, so here goes: *How come we're not upside down in mirrors?* You ask this and begin to understand the physics of mirrors at the very moment the words are leaving your mouth, and by the time he blinks that slow, deliberate blink and embarks upon an epic explanation, through which words and logic are applied at last to intuition, you understand completely the principles of reflection.

You find yourself crowding him into a corner and cut short your questions to kiss the strange mouth that you can't believe is the same mouth that smiles such a warm and charming smile (he does have a very nice smile, everyone agrees on that) but then snaps at a strawberry like a toad swallowing a moth, in three jerking, chomping bites. You remove the glasses from his eyes and say, in a voice like Ingrid Bergman's — is it Ingrid Bergman? no, it's someone irrelevant from some movie you don't like, but you're going to do it like Ingrid Bergman — so you say, *Oh darling, you had me at angle of incidence.*

❁　❁　❁

Actually, you do not do — would not do — would you? — any of those last few things although you loll for an hour in bed one morning thinking them up while your husband clatters and clinks things in the kitchen and finally — how you wish he would stop, just *stop* — brings you coffee with a touch of cream, no sugar, just like you like it, and two pieces of toast, one buttered, one jammed, just like you like them. He is feeling good today.

In only a year, much has been revealed, including the presence in your husband's liver of a virus, the treatment for which is more agonizing than the disease itself, which will eventually kill him, but not now, not soon, maybe not for many years—years and years!—so why must the treatment come now, in this fragile, fumbling first year of marriage? The daily doses of poison leave him worn, desiccated and patchy-haired. Yet he is unaccountably cheery! It is his nature, as it is the duck's to quack, the scorpion's to sting. Why now?

So much must be struggled through, a lifetime of struggling—how could you not have considered the outrageous length of the life before you?—with this man whom admittedly, admittedly, you love but—well, why not say it?—who came with an array of exasperating qualities that predated the discovery of the virus and have continued unabated even now, quite disproving the saintliness of the gravely ill. It's the mislaid paychecks, the professional cooking classes slept through or flunked, the birthday-gift Vespa purchased on your credit card and stolen before you even knew it was yours (he forgot the keys in the ignition), the time he left the window open and the cat fell three floors to the pavement and broke two legs.

It's other things too. It's even the things you love. That the animal he would be if he were any animal—if he could *choose* to be any animal—is a duck. You married a duck, you think now. How could you have married a duck? And yet, you can't bear to imagine forgetting these things. You can't bear to think that one day, your memory of his face will be foggy and painless, that one day (not soon! not soon!) you will not be there for the final moments, to bicker with nurses, sign forms, sleep in armchairs, and stroke the forehead of your ailing duck.

And now, this morning, after a period of grave dehydration and two days in the hospital hooked to pumps that filled him up again with fluids, he is cheery (of course) and almost wild with life. He wants to thank you, to do for you as you have done for him all these months, but how reluctantly, how peevishly you've done for him he hasn't noticed, or has refused to. You are a good wife. He brings you coffee and toast.

❖ ❖ ❖

When later that same morning you bump into the photographer in the halls of the art annex where you've gone specifically to bump into him, you feel yourself turning quite red, and then—oh vampiric treachery (or, more concretely, your refusal to eat the lovingly toasted toast)—you feel yourself turning quite pale, and you know you are going to faint, and in fact, the floor and the ceiling change places and you come out of the faint sprawled in his arms with that face hanging upside down over you. It's truly a troubling face.

It's the voice that's most confusing. It lumbers out like a friendly bear from a cave and says, "Just lie still until you're sure you can stand." And though he's still in that awful green shirt, he smells like sawdust and his hand is warm and enormous and sweeps the hair back from your forehead and holds it back and the voice rumbles, "She's okay. No, no, I've got her, she's okay," to the crowd of your colleagues and students gathering in the hall. The principal says to you, "Are you ill? Do you want a doctor?" and you say, "No doctor," and the Latin teacher with the crazily curled hair, the closest thing you have to a friend in this new place, squats down, leans in close to your ear and whispers, "Maybe you're pregnant."

You can see that he's heard this too, and there is an embarrassing, unspoken implication, though if pressed you couldn't name it, and he blinks his eyes, but you fling out your arms in search of the tile, knocking away his hand, and finally you distinguish up from down and you're standing and he's still on the floor. Now, you snatch up your things. You bolt.

When you see him again at lunch, he says, "Have you recovered from your *spell*?" and you say, "I have," and while you eat you find yourself leaning slightly in, slightly toward him, and you're afraid your colleagues will notice the leaning, but lean you must, so lean you do. He crosses his legs and his rubber shoe rests lightly against your shin. You pretend to be the table.

For the next day, you celebrate, secretly. You feel you have passed a test, and you will allow yourself outrageous and wicked flights of fancy. You are a somewhat pretty woman and you have always had suitors, some of them, including the one you finally (and unenthusiastically?) married, somewhat pretty themselves,

but your heart has chosen—well, it's overstating the case but—
your heart, after all these years of not knowing in the least what it
wants, has finally chosen—something else? You could be Beauty
to his Beast, Princess to his Frog. Concave to his Convex. You
will pack up your things, move out on the husband, divorce, and
marry immediately this brilliant, odd-looking man, and you will
have brilliant, odd-looking children, and you will adore them all,
and you will make them sometimes change their clothes, and you
will defend your miserable brood from contempt, and everyone
will wonder how such a delightful woman ended up with such a
categorically graceless lump of a man, or better, how such a categorically graceless lump of a man could deserve such a delightful
woman. It will be saintly, how you adore him.

This almost, but not quite—not nearly—actually only vague-
ly assuages the guilt of even thinking of abandoning a man who
will one day—not today, not tomorrow, not even soon!—be laid
low by his own liver. It is amazing how often this slips your mind.
You are appalled at the bifurcation of self that has allowed such
thoughts. At the forgetfulness that, among other things, causes
you in the middle of a grammar lesson, in front of fifteen mystified
fifteen-year-olds, to laugh hysterically at the double entendre in a
dangling (dangling!) modifier.

You concoct elaborate reasons to enter a room where he is,
and once in that room, you panic and make abrupt, inexplicable
exits. At school events you try to sit near him, not next to but
directly behind, perhaps. At an assembly in the old colonial church
that serves as a lecture hall and theatre, he is in front of you, just
to the right, and about fifteen minutes into the principal's tirade
against un-cited or fallacious internet sources, against plagiarism,
against cheating, you see him gazing at the ceiling, taking mental
measurements of the room, of the windows, and he turns around
and says softly, "I'm going to turn this place into a camera obscura." You notice that he has changed his shirt.

For a week you see him crossing from studio to woodshop to
lecture hall and back again with little wooden boxes and mirrors
tucked under his arms. He boards up the windows in the lecture
hall one by one. You run into him in the teacher's lounge, and in a
convulsion of glee he pulls from his wallet a mail-order invoice for
two dozen lenses. He rattles it at you. "By the end of the week!"
he says. Over lunch, he will speak of nothing but focal lengths and

apertures. In that he is speaking at all, this is a vast improvement in his social behavior, but in another sense this development is, for your colleagues, excruciating. You listen, conspicuously and intensely. To everyone's chagrin, you invite elaboration.

On Tuesday morning, between the usual announcements for quiz bowl practice and yearbook orders, he proclaims over the intercom the unveiling of the camera obscura. After the last bell, you come in with a group of other teachers, and you all take seats and drop your heads back to see the puddles of light on the ceiling above each window. One by one the others get up, say into the darkness *This is amazing, good work there, buddy*, and exit, and you finally realize that you and he are alone in the camera obscura.

He emerges from the shadows near you and says, "I've found that the best way to experience this is to lie down." And you both lie down in the aisles and watch the clouds move across the ceiling, the leaves flutter slowly in the trees, no accompaniment to this movement but the creaking of floorboards under your back, the rush of your breath, and the electric crackle (are you imagining this?) between your feet and his, no that's the click and hiss of an IV drip in the stillness of a hospital room, like the steady click and hiss of a camera on time-lapse, or actually it is his camera on time-lapse and it's recording the reflected movement of clouds. On the ceiling just above you are the main road and the gas station across from the school, its empty parking lot, utter stillness, and when a blurred human exits the gas station and moves away, toward the frayed edges of projected light, and then disappears into shadow, it's like discovering a code in the static of space. It is frightening and ominous and sad, it is a glimpse of the future of a memory.

You think: *We are watching forgetting. This is what forgetting looks like.*

You take a breath and say this, and there is no answer.

Half an hour passes and the two of you manage this much more conversation:

"Is it Tuesday?"

"Yes, it is Tuesday."

Finally, with nothing else to say, you pick yourself up from the floor, dust yourself off. You're right in front of the lens box, your head is blocking the sun—you can feel the hot coin of it on the back of your skull—and you idiotically make hand-shadows of an octopus swimming across the sky. There is no response. As you shuffle up the aisle, he says from the darkness, "Thanks for coming, come again," and you wonder if he means today, tomorrow, or nothing at all.

❖ ❖ ❖

One buoyant blue morning you are inexplicably crackling like cellophane, trembling with *agapē*, you are Isis, *agapē theon*, in spite of it all. This morning, this joy is a balloon that you tap with the tips of your fingers, a slow volley to the janitor, and he taps it back to you, and to the principal, and he taps it back to you, and to the Latin teacher with the crazy hair (now absolutely certain that you are "expecting," and you are, but what? what are you expecting?)—tap! with a flourish of wriggling fingers—and each of them smiles a true smile, a this-morning-in-June smile (although it is, of course, not June but nearly November).

It's the weather. It's only the effect of the weather.

It compels you to ask the photographer if he would like, after school, to go for a hike. When you call your husband, you don't even bother to lie. He has seen the photographer, granted, from a distance when picking you up from school, and you have composed a careful portrait besides—the rubber shoes, the off-kilter remarks. This could not be more than simply a hike. Your husband says, "Sure, okay. I can't do that with you. I want you to have someone to do that with."

❖ ❖ ❖

He has a cowboy-ish walk, very straight, and he strolls over boulders with no change in his posture, never bending, never grappling for a foothold, not at all like the scrambling squirrel you are. You and he climb up and up, up and up. Finally, you reach the top, the end, the vista, and there at the vista, there is a bench, only feet from a fierce drop-off.

You both sit on the bench with a little space between you. You hear him swallowing. A tumble of frivolous questions presses, but you wait. Your teeth are chattering, you are shivering, although it is easily 70 degrees. You pretend to enjoy the beautiful view.

"So," he says. "You moved here from the city."

"Yes."

"What did you like to do. In the city. For fun."

"Um," you say. You answer.

"I've never been to that city," he says.

"Well." You say something—too much—about the wind and the cold and the possums in the alleys. About the trains and the lake and the skyline and the ball teams and the bums, corners, taverns, noise, markets, neighbors, feral cats.

"You're homesick."

You are, you say. You are, but this is nice. It's nice to be out for a hike.

He blinks and you blink. There is something yet that needs to be said.

"Did you have a," he says. "A boyfriend."

"No—"

"In the city."

"I. Um."

When the word "husband" bobs to the surface like a drowned corpse, you feel like the world is upended and you will be shaken off. It's gone over the cliff, whatever it was that sat between you, you kicked it over the cliff and you can hear it whistling all the way down until it hits the bottom in a little puff of dust. Clearly, this is a bigger problem than you thought. You begin the funereal march back down the trail.

There is silence for the first fifteen minutes of the journey, and you wonder through this silence if there is something required of you, an apology, an abandonment of ethics, but then, suddenly, he is merciful. He points up into a tree, blinks once, twice, triumphantly, he says, "Look. Do you see it? A titmouse!"

❊　❊　❊

You are in a state of vapid waiting. Your skull is a lean-to and you're camped out under it, waiting for a change in weather. There is no change in weather. You start to blurt cryptic things to the colleagues, to the husband. Things like: *My skull is a lean-to and I'm camping out under it.* You feel you are speaking in rebus. You have trouble stepping outside the situation enough to determine exactly what is a problem, and exactly how much of a problem the problem is. You begin to suspect the problem is probably you.

At home, your husband resorts to antics. He requires your attention. (Of course he does. Of course, he requires your attention.) He begins with little gestures, like startling kisses on the neck while you stand petrified before an open cabinet in your kitchen, arrested by despair in mid-reach for a coffee cup. Or he grabs you in a hug, pins your arms to your body and holds tight against your squirming, saying *Who's my testy little kitty? Who?* Things escalate: he buys a wig, attempts soufflés. Finally, he throws up his hands and says, "I just don't understand."

"What?" you say. You poke with indifference at a deflated muck of egg whites and crabmeat that he's set before you for dinner. The wig, more joke than vanity—the "Special Bargain Quasimodo" that he ordered online in a fit of doubled-over hysterics, too red, not more convincing as hair than a clump of dried pine needles—is carefully arranged, seriously donned. His eyes are bloodshot. He looks dry again. His fingers. His ears. One spark and the wig would burst into flames.

"The sad," he says. "I just don't understand the sad."

✴ ✴ ✴

You decide to come clean. You will take your chances with your one friend, the Latin teacher, with her wild, mythic hair. A unicorn, she appears only to virgins, the pure of heart. Her eyes are wide and dewy, her gait is graceful, rolling—where her hips go, the rest of her follows. She told you once that she has exceptional—even mystical—powers of empathy, and you, earthbound flesh, believed her. You are beginning to know better, but all the same, she is a friend, your only friend, so you confide everything—the virus, the camera obscura—and when you do, she cringes from you, shields her face as if you have struck her. As if you have *struck* her, truly, and you think, my god, is it so awful, my god, is *this* my nature? She says, "Why are you telling me this? Why are you doing this to me?"

"To you?"

"This assault. On everything. On vows and love and—"

"But I didn't," you say, "I didn't *do* anything," and for the first time, it occurs to you this might be true. As for the unicorn, she will appear to you no more.

But screw the unicorns, you think, let's be more objective.

The fact *is*, before all this, before the obligating virus, you
had been nearing thirty and thinking that you'd better just pick
someone to love already and be done with it. Love, you told
yourself, after two critical, devastating failures, is a choice and not
a visitation, is not the shared transport of a 4 a.m. binge on Borges
and a can of sardines, is not transcendence or revelation, has no
empirical epistemology. It is like-mindedness on questions of dinner and dishes and laundry. It is, you have learned now, tolerance
of peculiar sounds from the bathroom, the daily jamming of needles into thighs. You pick someone, that's all. You pick someone
you like well enough and dig in. Ritual evokes reverence; every
injection, every slice of buttered toast conjures affection. Was this
cynicism or was it faith?

           ❊ ❊ ❊

At home, your husband has excused himself from living.
He has quit his job, or been fired—it is unclear which—and your
health insurance is the only thing between him and—what exactly?
This is also unclear. He plays video games. He has drawn the
living room curtains and sits cross-legged on the floor, his hands
working the controller, in darkness except for the glow of the television, and surrounded by plates of shriveled pizza, crumpled taco
wrappers, empty or half-full bottles of sports drink, all toppled and
scattered. When you ask him how he is feeling, he says, cheerily,
"Fine, fine! And how are you doing?" You might as well be greet-
ing each other over cantaloupes at the supermarket.

As one does in times of trial, when the truth is clear except to
the self, you have a dream. In your dream, your husband is a plate
of sushi. He is laid out in fleshy pinks and whites upon a bed of
rice and wrapped up neatly in cellophane. You peel back the cellophane—a naked, private, alarming sound—and pat the shrimp.
"I'm sorry," you say. "I'm sorry this is so hard."

At school, the photographer doesn't blink at you anymore,
and in fact, each of you pointedly ignores the other, but sometimes you still manage intentionally accidental contact. One day,
you have somehow both landed on a park bench in the courtyard
outside the annex. He is, incongruously, the sponsor of the school
yearbook, and three art girls dash over and flutter around him,
they want the key to the darkroom, and they cram themselves onto

the bench, shoving the two of you together. They tug and nip at him like puppies at an old hound dog. "Oh, Mr. So-and-So, you know you can trust us!" There is gray at his temples, and—you see that you were wrong, he is actually quite handsome. How could you have been so wrong? The art girls dash away again, leaving you thigh to thigh on the bench.

You say—you try to say—what can you say? You say nothing.

He says nothing.

Neither of you says anything.

When the fifth-period bell goes off, you rise together, and in the confusion of walking away, out of a habit that was never actual but only imagined, the two of you grab hands, you enfold fingers, you squeeze.

This startles both of you. It will never happen again.

One by One We Eased Lifeless Bodies Out

One by one we eased lifeless bodies out
of the classroom rubble, hand over hand
passed them swaddled in red and gray blankets
down our human line, from ugly slag
heaps to the church's makeshift mortuary.
I was the first to touch slack blue limbs, cold
as the River Taff where they once played free.
Now I'm here every night drinking late. Bold
visions of Black Friday wrestle my nerves,
work muscles into my sad, crazy dance.
No, not more than a pint of Welsh Brewers
is what it takes to restore a tired man's
soul, only I saw too much, I'm old
and there's no one left to take me home.

I.C. Rapoport, photograph

They are Kissing, in the Pub, Under One

They are kissing, in the pub, under one
dim bulb, cockeyed roof, starry pit of sky's
imperfect pearls, glint from the moon's glum
mouth, kissing. Kissing as the drained glass dries,
planets jig and reel away, urns are filled
and the columbine snakes its fragrance around
the mysterious hearts of youth. Hear her hip's
slender bell strike and clap, his chest pound,
the bone blade sound, when they are kissing.
Bodies long to break out, drag the mourning coat
behind — a lap dance among the living
as night scatters leaves down Aberfan Road.
Let them drink, taste the flesh they love and miss.
Let them honor the dead like that. Let them kiss.

I. C. Rapoport, photograph

For Emina

When Emina thinks of faces her thoughts are formed
by knowing the color of their hair, the manner of their eyes.
In terms of experience, there is no substitute for knowing

the way the light jumbled through the storefront windows
or the abscessed words spoken casually by the soldiers
to Emina's father. Her father leaning in, pleading, and then

quietly resigned, looking from his child to the men and back.
"Was he a soldier?" In terms of experience, there is no substitute
for knowing how much I wish it never occurred to me to ask.

"No, he owned a grocery. He wouldn't let them do it in front of me."
Among the breathing hard and some yelling, there is no substitute
in terms of spring or autumn, or noon and dusk, or playing cards

and years later the panic still driven nightly through your mind
like wild nails to wake you. The meager amounts I took
from her memory could not clarify in terms of place and time,

this before and after—the one shot, then the other.
Aided by scatterings Emina could speak of,
some communion held in my imagination. But change our roles

and this has no telling but through what I could not understand.
Now I'm the student. "Was he a soldier?" "No. . ."
There are not enough words to re-make the past into anything

but a story. "My father was killed." As she sometimes does,
Emina thinks about their faces. She cannot tell me specifically,
but this is what she thinks when I ask about Bosnia;

it's why her voice slips from school-girl
to someone who bares her teeth but does not bite.

The Naming

At first, what rouses you is the naming
of *nigga this* and *nigga that* — *nigga
I school yo' ass* — because you are the one
getting paid to school asses, correct English,
grade papers, and get kids going so they
can come to an understanding. You return
to high school to become ten months a minority,
not white and black, but rich and poor,
educated and uneducated. To name this
you must know, a fourteen-year-old
will slip from your roll for stabbing another boy.
The difference between you and him — between you
and the girl whose mother is a crack addict,
between you and the kid who has to care
for his siblings because his parents are around
but indifferent — is that on their side this is not pain,
this is the familiar, the unremarkable.
You never have to come to an understanding.
You are numb and not feeling because you
come from a yard where stars are not shy
in the city lights; not feeling this because you
have a yard to return to. These are inner-city sounds
made in the intricacies of elsewhere until the novelty
of the assumed and unaware is lessened,
and you think about the names on the papers
you mark, why *gangsta* is a euphemism for excellent,
and how India thinks it's funny to say, *Mista,
you know you my nigga*, knowing you'll never
quite get she means this as a compliment.
India calls you *nigga* before she smiles
out the door after the last bell, and you don't know
how to take your new position. And India
on her Friday-afternoon-way has no knowledge
(amid deafening hallways) of how she leaves you
in the exhaust of misplaced things. She carried you
for a moment, started a foundation, then let you fall
from her heft as lost as you began — the bricks

without mortar, the structure unstable.
All you can continue to say is, *Quana,*
this is a sentence fragment. Not really anything,
but *Kim, much improved. Vaska, you can do better.*
Sean, if you don't want to be here then leave.

Johanna Burton, *Out*, intaglio print

What Monsters You Make of Them

> Or, if thou wilt needs marry, marry a fool; for wise men
> know well enough what monsters you make of them.
> —*Hamlet to Ophelia, (III. iii. 140–41)*

As in cluster bombs, or eviscerated innocence,
or not enough money for food or heat, I'm grateful
for the sorrow of knowing
                                        most things in my life are well.
That I've sometimes had too much of the white male
past childhood never in want of anything
is not to sentimentalize why the refusal of the will is unsettling.
To only know need through desire and sometimes loneliness
highlights the difference between actualities and guesswork,
between having this happen to you
                                        and what teachers will say
was Hades to Persephone.
                        At bedtime my mother made her voice
tend to the mythic and I believed her. We were lucky enough
to allow nothing but the goblin, the wicked tempter,
the only hand of darkness to turn my mind
                                        to a limited kind of horror.
When the book closed, the pages were shelved
until some hero could make himself again. When the reporter
wrote about the man who molested his niece and three other girls,
I'm reminded happy endings have never done anything
to assuage a deep and steady sickening.
                                At the sentencing, my father
called the man an animal because he didn't know much else to say.
When the man protested he was something other, that is, than an animal,
my father, two months a jurist, not wavering, not raising his voice,
replied, *yes sir, you are*, and ironically confirmed
what had been known.
                        The man was a creature
who four legs, two legs, baying or balking, still breathed this air.
How the existence of this man was too much for most of us
was what my father wished to say. Whatever wrested amount of freedom
was meant to replace the satisfaction he took in children,

we all wished something worse—something unethical, not legally possible.
                     So say hallelujah to any horror that befalls that man.
Say hallelujah—what to make of him only gestures
towards the depth of indecency and selfishness;
actions that linger haughtily beyond measure—
                                   are too far from the heart—
which is one way for me to uncomfortably conjure Hades
and bind him to a more practical lesson. The man's thoughts
had some symmetry to concessions we make when making
an observance; say, as with Gustav Klimt, who painted his women nude
only to clothe their image after they'd left his studio.
Klimt worked on fantasy applied with brushes and misuse—
and in this manner, at the outlands of invention, with or without cause,
in pigment is an ownership. Approach another and say,
here are my hands to turn you.
                     As in, keep your hands to yourself.
And after the fantasy, finished and lying hands free—
feeling a little guilty?—wonder about the glossy-pictured girls
and the life they lead, and the life you imagine they lead.
                     Not that they all must be meager.
Not, at least, when they were your own,
when their likeness was as earnest as your flesh,
their trade parceled out slick for the viewership and just long enough
to stave off some loneliness. Claim them the darling you'd love
in dresses, spinning, dancing on Saturday night. Treat them well.
Set them out the door and clothe them from an imaginary wardrobe.
Let the uncle be done with his niece and imagine nothing terrible
had happened. Take turns at augmenting, and know how easily
a sitting can turn into a study of sex, can become the moment
that is make-believe, and watch—presto—the staff is now a snake.
                     The audience watches and hardly questions
what and who would lead an actor to speak in such a way,
or into this line of work. *Try it again, this way.*
How much acting can there be in the act of copulation?
In the editing room, whether with organ or instrument,
the separation of frames is tailored to suit our needs (as in animals),
and at museums I've seen how irrelevant Klimt has made her clothes.
                     And here is the sentiment again,
this practice of being faithfully enamored with the nuisance
of particular heartbreak.

                                    Like when the guidance counselor, not knowing
I knew enough to fill in her *you don't want to know* with actualities,
continued with the silly speech she gave most teachers,
that is, decay is a difficult thing to whip.
                              A week earlier, on the last day
K was present in my class I walked an almost empty hallway after school
and heard this argument—*But, I love you . . .* at first my impulse to . . .
and then Marcus's reply, *You hoe. You'd suck anyone's cock*
I told you to. And having closed the gap between us, Marcus
turned to me forgetting himself, or not caring, said, *she would you know,*
affirming, not his stupidity, or K's abuse, but my helplessness,
having known what'd been going on for weeks—
what it was leading up to—and unable to do anything about it.
Marcus would pick K up and they'd drive around—friends' houses,
fast food, go and see a movie—and she'd make love to him,
and it went like this until she failed to fulfill whatever he had
in his mind as essential.
                              And K, the girl who, shortly after her mother
kicked her out, told me, *and don't tell anyone,* how she was pregnant.
And two months later the only thing different is the boy, but again,
I'm pregnant. K, who cultivates the kind of imagination it takes
to possess the reproductive cycle of a fruit bat—or rather, difficulties
less resigned to desperate—creates something which belongs to her
and cannot be taken as anyone else's. Even if it is only the intangible,
as in paintings, or the story you are hearing, or how in ninth grade I imagined
the great unchecked weeping of Demeter as she called into the pit
for her daughter. And all the flowers wilted. Only in some fucked-up way
does K believe fantasies will facilitate a home-life or opportunity or autumn.
Over a matter of weeks,
                              Marcus took his and I was too distant
to insist on his talent for treating people like he is better than them,
like he is smarter than he really is, like he is just an animal.
When one of his teachers called his mother to say
he was not meeting his potential,
                                    she insisted her son was a prince,
because all he needed to know he learned, not in school,
and not from any white person she ever knew.
How like a prince crowned by cardboard, who stops reason
in favor of what feels right. As in, less than an animal,
who as if grateful for the opportunity to be blinded, too tired to care

what has kept him intrigued, without thought, like a moth at light,
finds it difficult to navigate, instead pulsing through selfishness
with dignity. There was nothing as believable in any bedtime story
as I wanted to believe in K.

Marcus looked at me as if what he said was scripture.
And K could not shake the grittier stuff, let boys unstrap, unbutton,
and play secretly in not so secret places. And Marcus conjures a Hades
unteachable in any ninth-grade classroom. He conjures a man able to tolerate
barren places and call them lovely, a boy who helps further stifle what was
not yet dead but on the way to dying. Like vicious dogs, or an arsonist
watching—in the worthlessness of words—the impulse
that makes the pomegranate seed some terrible consummation.

Triptych with Birds

for my mother

1

It will rain, and all night it will rain, and the waters
will run so dark with tannin for days that the rivers
will not slip free of their slick, black boots. And she

will be adrift in the glass-bottomed boat
of delirium and be, by dawn, beyond reach
even though I will have slept the whole night beside her.

Look, she will say, *I can see straight down
and into what I knew would happen: my body,
so hungry to live, eating itself.* I know

the logic of fever is like the logic of a dream
and that the body's appetite can sabotage
what it loves best, and I will begin

to dream of mouths where no mouths should be.
The storm will clear and all afternoon
the clouds will move loosely over and the wind

will chase its pennants through the grass and sunlight
test its tongue along the hedge backs, polishing
the coinage of the leaves so they shine

like the worn soles of shoes. So much burning
without flame. What matters is not
what I'll remember, but how I'll remember it: not

that her breathing will be difficult, but that it will be
almost secret, like the first bird waking — no singing,
yet, but a delicate stirring in the leaves of the escalonia;

not that the first bird will arrive at the feeder,
but that a bullfinch will arrive and cling
to the slim basket of seeds, his waistcoat on fire.

2

I am up at first light, crows
passing over,
a run of snips in the sky's blanched awning,
the world's black lining; on the lawn,
two doves in matching collars
of pewter, and a solitary,

robin, that beguiling blaze of his chest
an invitation, like a man unbuttoning
his shirt in public

one button too far. Rain on the helmets
and throat guards of the stonechats' dark armor.
Amid the fuss there is always one, grounded

by damage, waiting in the grass: a chaffinch,
his left foot crushed and twisted,
who cannot get a toehold on the thin wire mesh

of the feeder. Every morning I find him, gleaning
what the rest in their enthusiasm
let go — whole seeds, crumbles of suet —

and what I feel is more than relief.
It is a kind of gratitude. And so late in my life.
My mother sleeps on, well past noon,

and her sleeping feels like a separate life.
I am alone, but I have not been abandoned. I watch
that bird and the way his wings close

perfectly, against his body
like envelopes being sealed; how he waits,
without fuss or fanfare, and misses nothing.

3

Out in the bay, a small boat, its rubber skin
glistening like a seal's. Three small figures in scarlet
lifejackets. The blue clarity

of deep water. Blue. Azul. A shadow
is bluest when the body casting it has already
vanished. I sit with her, inside those pockets

of radiance that open up within a storm,
and *who's there* she cries, startling
awake each time the room becomes wild

with a sudden yawn of light and I
feel it too: a door opening
directly from this world and, for a moment,

it is everywhere—blue of pressed breath, blue
like a taste of history; the fascia-like glare
on the spine of a book forced open

too far and a body
to which similar things are happening. Afterburn
of a struck match. There are no blues

in the caves of Lascaux.
The masks of the Incas were blue. A hawk
glides in, low, over the garden, and the birds

at the feeder in their panic rise up
as the crucifix of its shadow passes
over the grass. And so death

has slipped into the poem. On the color wheel,
blue is closest to white. Out in the bay
the small boat slides behind the curtain

of the sun's late glare on the water.
I am thinking of Giotto's Saint Francis
talking to the birds, how the birds stutter down

like scarlet bark against the blue's
high-minded backdrop; how he painted in
a few extra so that he could simply

wipe them, deliberately, from the canvas; how
their shadows remain, like a dream
of a memory about birds. And I

understand, now, what he's saying: that there
was a body here, then it was leaving. Then gone.

In a Golden Boat

The Bengali poet Tagore watched a golden boat come ashore. It was singing with its sails & then taking his golden paddy with it. The Slovene poet Srecko Kosovel called his unpublished manuscript *The Golden Boat* after Tagore's poem. Kosovel has a poem of his own about a golden boat:

I Went for a Ride

I went for a ride in a golden boat
across the red waters of evening
all through the trees
and along the grassy shore.
I was rowing,
I, the golden boatman.

But a storm blew in
and the sun fell
from its height.
As though everything else
less golden, shone forth
more clearly, more alive,
I stepped ashore.

The red clouds tore
from my heart.
I saw them
I followed them
across the world.

Translated by Ana Jelnikar and Barbara Siegel Carlson

The Golden Boat is also the name of a poetry translation workshop that brings poets who speak different languages and come from many countries together to translate each other's work. It is an apt name for a workshop that is both transportive and transformative. For the last two summers I participated in the Golden Boat International Poetry Translation Workshop founded and organized by Slovene poet Iztok Osojnik. Along with Ana Jel-nikar, a Slovene translator, and Slovene poet Barbara Pogocnik, Osojnik has brought 20-30 poets and translators together from several European countries, the United Kingdom, and the United States to Slovenia to translate each other's poetry for one week.

The 2006 workshop was held in Skocjan, a 350-year-old village built directly on top of the Skocjan Caves. The village had been abandoned over the last 30 years and was recently reno-vated when the site of Skocjan Caves was inscribed on the Unesco World Heritage List in 1986.

Walking up and down the narrow, empty village roads above the cave to and from the picnic table near the church where we often met, and also following the underground paths of the cave together, I started to see the whole experience of translating as if I were exploring the passages hidden in both my own language and those of the others. Most of us didn't know each other when we arrived. There was Jouni from Finland, Simona from Ro-mania, Christophe from France, Maria and John from England, Iztok, Ana, Barbara and Primoz from Slovenia, and myself from the United States. By the end we felt connected as though many borders had been crossed, and trails created through the language of poetry.

The two poems that follow were translated at the workshop in Skocjan.

Après-Midi Paris, Peu Après, Musée d'Art et d'Historie du Judaisme: Bracelets Or et Argent

Dans la vitrine deux bracelets
deux bracelets soleil et lune, à
soleil et lune argent de la lune

à soleil et lune or du soleil
or du soleil et argent de lune
de lune se tournent, de soleil.

De tresses d'or, de tresses d'argent
d'argent les deux bracelets se tiennent
se tiennent d'argent les tresses lune

se tiennent d'or les tresses soleil
soleil les coffres d'or qui dépassent
dépassent les coffres lune argent.

Voyage autour du poignet soleil
soleil les deux bracelets de lune
de lune, de soleil or, argent.

Later in the Afternoon in Paris at the Museum of Jewish Art and History: Gold and Silver Bracelets

Two bracelets in the window
  two bracelets sun and moon, to
    sun and moon the silver of the moon

to sun and moon the gold of the sun
  gold of the sun and silver of the moon
    Of the moon that turns, of the sun.

Of the golden braids, of the silver braids
  of the silver of two bracelets braiding
    they are braiding the silver of moon

braiding the gold of the sun
  a gold chest rising from the sun
    as the silver chest rising from the moon.

Circling the wrist of the sun
  the sun two bracelets of the moon
    of the moon, of the gold sun, silver.

Translated from the French by Barbara Siegel Carlson

Moja Napaka

Moj namen, da bi te srečal, se ni
posrečil. Hodil sem po krajih, kjer sem
te enkrat videl, razmišljal sem o ponovitvi.
Bila je moja napaka.
Vsa odstopanja naj bi našla
svoje potrditve v standardnih primerih.
Obračal sem se, da bi te zagledal.
Bili so vsi drugi, razen tebe.

A šlo je samo za ljubezen na
prvi stopnji. Veter je
zavihral obešeno perilo,
v glavnem mestu se je začela sobota.
Ven grem in upam, da je ne
bom ponovil. Drži se me trohica
pričakovanja, vendar se ne bom obrnil.
Mogoče je v zraku namen, da te srečam.

My Mistake

My intention to happen upon you
failed. I walked around places
where I saw you once, kept hoping.
That was my mistake.
I resigned myself to standards
of acceptable behavior.
I would look around for a glimpse of you.
There were others, but not you.

It was only a matter
of first love. The wind clasped
at the wash on the line.
Saturday started out rough at home.
I left hoping I wouldn't repeat
the same mistake. There's a tiny twig
of expectation, but I won't hold on. Maybe
it's just in the air, my intention to meet you.

Translated from the Slovenian by Barbara Siegel Carlson

John Milisenda, *Orange County Fair*, photograph

Lions and Carnivals

The day before Diwali, an Indian festival of lights, I rode my bicycle to the Zamindar's house to pick up my mother. In order to plant my feet firmly on the ground I had to dismount from the seat and straddle the crossbar and, in the process, I happened upon my face reflected on the handlebar.

A forest of facial hair seemed to be encroaching into a mount of freshly erupting pimples on my cheeks. I blew on the handlebar and watched a spreading mist of air engulf my image, and what a relief!

Because, now, I could choose to remember my face any way I wished and how I wished to remember it was the way it looked before I was ruined by adolescence. Adolescence ushered in bad looks. And in my case, a list of responsibilities longer than the Kashmiri-Kanyakumari Express, Kanyakumari being the name of my town.

Anyone who had employment in our town appeared to be employed by the Zamindar and every gainfully employed man seemed to exist for the sole purpose of making Diwali that year a memorable occasion for the Zamindar, our local kingpin.

As I waited for my mother to appear in front of his mansion, I noticed an army of men hanging from the roof of the house, like a cluster of butterflies, trying to install electric lights. Men were blossoming out of tree trunks trying to trim down the branches in preparation for the fireworks and men were sprouting on his portico, large enough to host a world football match, hosing it down in preparation for the family meal.

Through the glass window, I could see the Zamindar himself standing under a whirring ceiling fan, which made the few remaining hairs on his scalp stand in full attention. As he studied the handiwork of his many employees, he seemed to be leisurely rubbing his rotund bare belly, counterclockwise, as if his soul was resting in there somewhere.

That abdominal girth, thanks to his refined tastebuds, was shaped by women like my mother, who cooked for him from time to time.

That day, after having toiled in his kitchen all day, my mother arrived looking every bit like an over-steamed, underground tuber and did not so much as give me a glance. She climbed onto the crossbar of my bicycle and kicked on the wheel, as if alerting an idling horse.

"Let's go, son," she said. "Gallop away."

"You did it again, didn't you?" I asked as I pedaled up a slope.

"Those girls are off to the carnival," my mother said, making it clear she was ignoring me. Also that she was more interested in a speeding bus. A tomato-colored bus with decorative palm leaves on the windshield was crossing a bridge.

I noticed the upside-down reflection of the bus on the estuary as it rolled on. About one hundred young girls were screaming and chanting and banging on their banjos. Some of their scalps were shaved, the nudity of the bald heads exaggerated with sandalwood paste smeared all over them.

Girls that age pretended boys my age were invisible. One of them pulled off a headscarf and waved at my mother. She grinned from east to west.

"I know you did it, Meena," I said as I pedaled hard on my bare feet.

The climb was steep, the sun merciless, and I was breathless. I tried to study my mother's face as I gasped for air but she refused to meet my gaze.

"It'll take the Zamindar one year to figure out they are missing something," she said sounding confident as an entrepreneur.

"They may have plenty," I said. "But it belongs to them, like it or not, Meena."

"Not anymore."

My mother stared into the empty day, her eyes squinting into slits. But not one stray emotion seemed to mar her face.

Just then, I felt a surge of anger and fantasized about pushing my mother off the bicycle. I felt sad that I had not thought of doing something drastic to her at the railroad crossing.

My mother's hair smelled like smoke spewing out of wet wood, her parched lips blended into the desertscape of her face. The creases of her blouse were flooded with sweat and her glass bangles jingled about on her vanishing wrists. Even that harmless, pealing sound of cheap glass drove me insane.

My mother let go of the handlebar and waved hysterically at the kids on the bus. Her bangles tinkled ever so much, and my bicycle swerved every which way. That was enough to make me regret that I had not seized an opportunity to chuck her into the estuary.

I kept pedaling, and with each agonizing push, she seemed to get heavier.

"I am ashamed, Meena," I said.

"I am not, son," she said.

I pedaled past the bridge. Down below, a shrimp boat puttered and a few bare-chested kids looking like tadpoles swam around it in circles. An old man in a crisp white shirt tossed a handful of oranges overboard and the kids went diving after the suicidal oranges.

My mother's hair blew into my face and I saw how her thick neck was draped with beads of sweat instead of a gold chain, how her hands stretched out on the handlebar with dense veins coursing through them, and I started to feel sorry for her.

I thought about how she was doomed to a life as a servant, cooking for others, feeding others, cleaning after them, feeding, cleaning, cooking, always caring for someone other than herself. I thought about how she seemed imprisoned inside one kitchen or another, and how her only hope for escape from this fate was if her children became somebody worth becoming.

It was so hot even as the sun was dying out for the day that my bicycle tire smoked from rubbing against the asphalt. I barely mentioned stopping for a short while and, before I convinced myself, my mother jumped off the moving bicycle and scurried alongside for a few yards to slow herself down to a complete stop. She started to puff from the effort and dropped to the ground on her knees. On all fours, she crawled towards the shade and propped herself against the trunk of a neem tree.

All around us people were hurrying about as if they feared they couldn't make it into tomorrow on time. There was the smothering smell of freshly cooked food wafting through the air while the world got ready for the Diwali feast.

Something in my body informed me that I was hungry. And something else reminded me that I hadn't eaten in a day or two. Or two or three. Food, amongst other necessities, was a rarity in my family.

"What do you have today?" I asked, climbing over a nearby rock. "Anything to eat?"

My mother pulled aside her *palu* and went fishing inside her blouse. She groped around for a while and pulled out something shiny. My eyes widened.

I gasped. "I thought you did eatables only."

"I thought so too," my mother said. "Until I wasn't."

On her palm, she held a jewelry box, dazzling mercilessly with a few hundred precious gems embedded on it.

She impatiently snapped open the jewelry box and emptied its contents onto her thigh.

"See, it has one hundred carvings of pin-sized elephants. All made of ivory," she said, and picked one of the elephants and studied it keenly. "Look, they even have tusks."

I stared at a pin of an elephant lying in her sweaty palm.

They were indeed the tiniest carvings of elephants I have ever seen. And they did have tusks carved to size. If you hadn't seen those tusks, you'd think you couldn't see those tusks.

"The police crooks will come after you for this, Meena."

My mother rested her hand on my shoulder and giggled.

"Let them take me to prison and put me out of my misery," she said, laughing harder, as if the notion got more interesting the more she thought about it. Her hand went fishing inside her waist and out came a banana leaf wrapped around a juicy *ladoo*, sweating butter.

"Here, son," she said handing me a globe-shaped *ladoo*. "I made five hundred of these today and guess what I got in return? A stinking glass of watery buttermilk. Looked and tasted like someone's puke."

It made me sad to think about why she must bother going to work for the Zamindar when her best compensation for all her efforts was someone else's vomit. How pathetic my mother's life was that the absurdity of going to work only matched the absurdity of not going to work.

"So . . ." my mother said as she handed me the treat. "I paid myself a small bonus, you see."

I hesitated but took the *ladoo* and quickly shoved it into my mouth.

For a long while, my mother watched me chomp on it like nothing in the world meant more to her than watching her pimply son greedily ingesting a *ladoo*.

A smile of joy appeared on her tired face and refused to disappear. Only her eyelids closed shut and she seemed to doze off.

The air was so hot that the world started to dance all around me. My mother leaned over and rested her head on my lap. Another tomato-red bus filled with young girls rolled by, tooting its horn.

"I want to take you kids to the carnival," my mother whispered.

Her eyes remained shut as if she was watching the images of the proposed trip. "You and your sister, Usha kutty."

❋ ❋ ❋

That evening, I found my father sorting out wildflower petals by their varying shades, into neat little piles. His beard was so long it had mopped up some flower petals that swayed in the wind like colorful prayer flags. My sister Usha kutty—we called her Usha kutty because she was so tiny she looked like she could still be nursing even though she was six years old—would have to go fishing into his beard to dislodge them, one at a time.

My mother sat in the kitchen blowing on a stubborn wooden stove which was smoking furiously and making us cry charcoal-laden tears. I watched her rub her eyes dry on her blouse and thought about how hungry she must be, too. It made me sick to think about it, and I wanted to be as far away from her as possible.

"You are a fool to work as a coolie," my father admonished me when I told him I had to work on Diwali day.

"Never ever turn into a worker bee, son. Always . . ." he said with his finger scraping the underside of the sky. "Always, stay on the side of royalty. You hear me?"

I heard him but there was little to say to him. The anger that had been reserved for my mother shifted to my father. If he were useful, half as useful as nature intended for humans to be, she would have been a different kind of a mother for me and Usha kutty.

Usha kutty could walk past a busy textile store and add up complicated sales figures in her head. She was faster than a calculator. She had had her sixth birthday not long ago and no one remembered it except me, but the sad part was that it hadn't occurred to my petal-sorting father or my *ladoo*-lifting mother that they should be sending her to school.

At fourteen, I had to quit school and start working at the harbor as a coolie. My mother said I was growing too old, too fast, although she and I knew why. Once I was even offered a bribe by an inspector and it was just too tempting.

"Na, na, no, Saar," I said. "I can't do it, Saar. My mother will kill me."

That day, I remember how the inspector spit out a mouthful of betel leaves onto a telephone pole on Pier Twelve, next to Paris Corner. It looked like someone had bled all over it. Every time I walked by Pier Twelve, I remembered how my heart raced when he opened his small suitcase and showed me stacks and stacks of crisp *rupee* notes. I forgot the whole business after the rains washed away the stains on the telephone pole.

Kids in the neighborhood were playing with their Diwali firecrackers and the smell of sulfur filled the air. By then my father had moved to his swing-seat, where he embarked on his next project for the day, which was to tirelessly stroke his luxurious beard.

My father thought big thoughts.

His survival plans for our family involved conquering the planet, taking over the universe. He hatched a new business plan every day and shared it with anyone who was willing to listen to him. He always made sure to whisper, so no one else could overhear.

In the real life that we shared with him, my father sold old newspapers to street cobblers.

"Soon, I'll teach you how to be a Maharajan. Watch and learn, son," my father said, rocking himself gently and wearing a very regal expression.

"I'm already a Maharajan's son, appa," I said, as I patted cow dung and sun-dried it.

My mother tried to contain a sneeze with her *palu* and her face turned crimson.

"I am too old for the carnival, Amma. Take Usha kutty if you want," I told her, hoping not to report to work on Diwali day, but instead to bring myself to the estuary lazing behind our home.

There was a promise of an empty day in front of me, the banyan tree by the estuary looked generous, and the sea breeze had the same intentions as I did of dreaming that day away.

I might even consider allowing my father entry inside my dream, which was easy to do. My father was charming and utterly useless, extremely opinionated and prone to calling the sun the moon, and it was all so easy to encourage him and then to dismiss him.

"We are going," my mother said. "And I did not carry one hundred elephants on my chest for nothing. That's settled."

She gave up on the stove and started to comb Usha kutty's hair, tugging on the knots and repositioning her head as though she had detached it for cleaning purposes.

"I want to go with you, Amma," Usha kutty consoled her, and I felt that nauseating feeling of guilt and pity rise inside me. I squatted on the laundry stone and sank my head into my knees.

It sometimes seemed to me that someone must have removed a shelf in my heart reserved for tender mother-love and replaced it with solid rocks.

God should strike me with lightning for not showing my mother any gratitude. The more she sacrificed for us, the more I resented her. The more she denied her own joys, the more entangled I felt, and the more suffocating it all became.

I said a small prayer asking God to forgive me for such impudence and offered to go the temple every Friday and prostrate myself in front of him. I would try to cultivate genuine love for my mother, I promised God. Could He please show me how to mold pity into love?

"It'll cost three of us 84 rupees. *Eiyo yappa,* too much," said our little mathematician.

"I'll manage the money," my mother said, tugging on my sister's hair mercilessly. "Usha kutty, add dinner for three at Suri Poti's and tell me how much more."

"What about me?" said my father from his swing-seat on the portico. "You'll need a man to take you all."

No one said anything.

Only a dripping faucet in the yard dared to make a steady, rhythmic sound. A struggling ant clambered onto a mound of dirt in the middle of the puddle, only to have the eddy suck it back into the morass.

My mother filled an aluminum cup with the dripping water and helped herself to a long drink. Her neck strained from trying to gulp down the water in a hurry and her Adam's apple ran up and down her neck like a fleeing mouse. "That's dinner for me," she said. Grabbing a mat from behind the kitchen door she disappeared inside the storeroom.

"We're to vacate this house," Father said to no one in particular. "Fools. They don't know what they are doing. Asking me to leave just because I did not pay their *naiya paisa* rent. Some day . . ."

"Some day, they'll come crawling to my feet." My sister finished his sentence for him and my mother locked the door behind her.

❉ ❉ ❉

Forty years ago, when my father was eight years old, my grandfather managed The Burma Oil Company. Life was divine, my father would say, and talked about his life then as if he were the son of the last Viceroy.

When the British left the country, my grandfather, a staunch supporter of the Occupation, found himself without a job. Consequently, my father had to be taken out of school so he could follow his father around, whenever he went looking for work.

My father did the math, my grandfather did the talking and between the two of them they managed to land a job as a bookkeeper for the Trustee of Meenakshi Temple in the outskirts of Kanyakumari.

My grandfather tossed the key to the Temple safe on my father's lap and said, "Here boy, you miss one *paisa*, you'll pay for it with one of your bones."

And every evening, my father added up all the donations in cash, accounted for all the donations in kind, and kept scrupulous records.

The amount my grandfather got paid to do that job was not worth his time, so the son was hired for nothing. And to make it worth his time, my grandfather had other plans.

Leaving my father to do the balancing of the books, he walked down the river path, hiked his *dhoti* way up to avoid getting wet, and waddled across the currents to the other side. Everyone in town knew about his mistress, who lived amongst the field workers in a hut. People even said that one of the retarded children, Muttu paiya, was his illegitimate son.

When I was growing up, I remember Muttu paiya periodically stopping by at our house and my father being kind to him. He would make my mother feed him even if all of us had to go without food.

I remember when Usha kutty was just a baby, Muttu paiya came to our house. We were living next to SLB High School then.

He must have been about my father's age but looked young, perhaps because no serious thought ever entered his head. He still wore his boxer shorts and inside his pockets he usually carried the most interesting things I have ever seen. Once, it was a porcelain bird that would whistle, once it was a small photo frame and once, something I fell in love with, a 3-D picture of a young woman with golden hair who would wink at you with her golden eyes. But it was her golden breasts, proud and bare as mangos, that I wanted to wink back at. I had to have that picture.

It seemed more useful, more worthy of its beauty, inside my pocket than inside his pocket. So out it went from his pocket and in it fell into mine, and out it came again when I climbed inside an empty hot water boiler in our bathroom.

Outside, Muttu paiya sat on our laundry stone the whole time, serenading. He sang the same line of a film song over and over again for two hours straight, which I did not mind. What I did mind was being discovered by my mother.

"Here you are, of all places," she poked me with firewood. Her hand reached over the boiler and with her glass bangles merrily jingling away, she handed me an ounce cup filled with warm milk to bring to a family down the street.

"Get the money from them and buy some rice," she said. "We are to feed our minstrelsy sitting out there."

I stood upright suddenly. I made it. My trouser did not. My picture did not.

The trouser was a puddle around my ankle.

The picture flew across the room, took its time exiting through the door, slid under a coir bed in the veranda, circled towards the grinding stone and miraculously landed back at my mother's feet.

Her eyes migrated behind her ears. It was hard to know if it was I or the picture that had caused the dislocation.

"Who gave you this dirty picture? What were you doing?" Then she dropped the picture. Her blouse was wet with her milk.

The lie was what got to her, she said. She and I knew otherwise.

Her hair came unbraided. She shook her head and her exuberant hair cascaded to her waist.

With my mother, when you see a trickle, you prepare for the flood.

She grabbed the baby, ran outside and screamed at the top of her voice.

"Take them back," she said, holding up the child in a defiant rejoinder at the looming skies. It sounded like she was addressing someone up there that she could actually see. As if someone up there had consulted with her before they gave her the children in the first place.

"Take them all back," she screamed and sobbed. "I did not go hungry to raise liars. I did not sell my own breast milk to raise liars and thieves. And look, what kind of a child I'm raising . . ."

She was inconsolable. My father sat on his swing-seat and I noticed how his hand-held fan moved a tear collecting in his eyes.

"What did I do to deserve this?" she screamed hysterically at her imaginary maker.

I walked into the kitchen and opened a jar of chili powder, grabbed a handful and shoved it into my mouth. My eyes watered mercilessly and I coughed incessantly all night. I couldn't speak for two days, but my mother heard me even without a word. She understood me. That was my promise to her. And I never ever wished to disappoint her again.

❖ ❖ ❖

On Diwali morning, the sun seemed ambivalent about its time of arrival, and the four of us were already walking along the riverbank towards the carnival grounds. The sound of an occasional fish jumping and splashing was the only sound interrupting our meditative silence. A brooding army of trees marched towards us, and I kept dreaming about being back inside my gunnysack on the veranda, sleeping to the smell of fresh coir, sleeping to the sound of singing mosquitoes. My eyes pleaded to be blind again.

But not Usha kutty.

Usha kutty was wide awake and skipped on her tiny feet for every few steps she walked, in order to keep up with us; her eyes were open wide.

I had no business being at the carnival. I realized that even more strongly the moment we fell in step with nine thousand, nine hundred and ninety-nine other families, marching about in a daze which said they did not want to be there either.

The only purpose of being there, it seemed to me, was to stop someone from drawing a line of connection between any of us. And if accidentally my family came close to me or spoke to me, I had rehearsed an expression that told the world all too clearly that I had no clue who these people were. Even my sister.

She was busy talking, not about the million people all around her, but about something that even a million people would not be interested in listening to. Like the scum floating on a pond far away. Like the Midland Goods Train that was late crossing the bridge that day. Like the connection between balding men and English newspapers.

My dad led the pack and, like a true alpha lion, had to be a few feet ahead of the rest. His head was held high as if just his nose yearned for the sun, his hands clasped into a knot behind his back. He adjusted his gait, throwing a leg forward and then letting the rest of the body flow after it. His head rocked between 10 o'clock and 2 o'clock and then swept back to 10 o'clock. This way, he was able to study the world presented to him in some reasonable fashion.

My mother appeared to be walking, but when mother walked it was hard to tell the difference from when she ran or just sat. She looked as if she was patiently teaching an amoeba the beauty of locomotion.

A lion that had been recently captured in Gir forest had been transported to the carnival just that morning. "Folks, come and see with your own two eyes," a voice on the loudspeaker beckoned in eight different languages.

Usha kutty covered her ears and pointed to the picture of an unlucky lion striking a deadly pose. From behind the curtains came the deadly roar of an animal who must surely resent his newfound stardom.

"It's him," Usha kutty said, pointing at the picture of the mighty lion. Her eyes were filled with awe and fear. "I see him every night. He is the one who prowls about trying to eat us."

Usha kutty *refused* to walk past the booth. My mother tried to drag her away.

"This lion is not dumb enough to come eat mere bones like us, stupid girl. He'll go to the Zamindar's house if he wants food. Now get up and walk."

Usha kutty sat on the ground and kicked up a dust cloud, refusing to budge. For my mother, giving an instruction and then punishing you for not following her instruction happened simultaneously. Usha kutty screamed louder, and my mother responded with glorious verbal bouquets while the lion roared on.

I hoisted Usha kutty on my shoulders and ran across the booth.

"You're smart enough to divide the number of lions in this world by the number of fools in this world, and look at you, all scared," I said.

She sobbed from the comfort of my shoulders but even with the urgency of a river of snot heading for her mouth, she took some time out, in order to brag. "Also, I can times the amount it costs to put your head into the lion's mouth and the answer is . . ." she said.

"Do let us save some numbers, so we can eat them when we get hungry," I said.

Was she hungry? I asked. No, she was not hungry. She was thirsty. Very thirsty. A soda?

"No rupee, no paisa," I said.

A man with a sword for a moustache, dressed in black and red, handed her a soda bottle.

My mother lurched and snatched it from my sister's hand. She dumped the orange soda over a rock and stood reverently as if anointing it.

We watched the fizzy water gurgle its way and empty out with a resounding burp.

"We are not beggars," she said. "Not yet. Your father is working on it but not yet, children."

"We can be thieves, children," my father said. "But we are not beggars, remember that."

My mother's stare was a fire hazard.

"Why don't you buy her something, if you are so proud?" my father asked. "Find some change in one of those many hiding places in your body and buy something for your child, will you? We're all dying of thirst here." He pulled his unbuttoned shirt off his neck to let some breeze into his body.

My mother secured her yards of sari in many specific locations to ensure her money stayed where it belonged.

"The children will eat the best meal of their lives today," she said and suddenly started to walk so fast that we could not keep up with her.

❖ ❖ ❖

My father insisted on an air-conditioned room at Suri Poti's restaurant. The server boy was perhaps fourteen years of age and had a fresh growth of beard. And I noticed that ugliness was creeping into him too.

"Thambi, get us the best family room," my father said.

We sat facing a window. Outside there was a pink building looking like a wrestler, broad-shouldered and unintimidated, as if planning to invade the space around it. Usha kutty said she could do multiples of the number of cockroaches hiding behind the curtain on the window.

"Did you see that house?" my father said to me proudly. "The inspector owns it."

"The inspector didn't get that rich without stepping on someone's head," my mother said. She looked very pleased with herself with that comment and sat back on her chair with some authority.

"So what's wrong with bettering yourself in this world, eh, woman? Unlike you, that man knows how to succeed. I see nothing wrong with that. Some man is willing to offer a bribe, some man is willing to accept a bribe. I call it supply and demand. I call it fair market economy. Petty people like you, with petty thoughts, petty actions, won't understand . . ."

"Appa, one day will we be living in a house like that?" Usha kutty mercifully interrupted.

The server boy stood on his one foot, since the other foot had only two toes left and he seemed to give it a well deserved rest.

"Bring us your Super-Duper-Deluxe-Special meal. Four plates," my father told him. "And for Usha kutty, some rose milk and, for my queen here, some savory Badushah."

"Appa," I said. "No, Appa."

The server boy hopped on his one foot to the end of the stairs, slid down the side railing and disappeared.

"Appa, you can't do this," I pleaded.

My father leaned towards me, picked up the hem of the tablecloth to cover his mouth and whispered.

"See, that woman sitting across from us?"

"Our mother?"

"She owns the State Bank of India and she is buying."

My father cleared his throat.

"Now comes the big surprise," he announced.

Anytime he announced a surprise it was Usha kutty's job to get down on her knees to plead with him to share it with the family.

But that day, she couldn't tear herself away from her rose milk to put on a charade.

"Do you all have a grain of curiosity left in you, or are you all dead?" my father bristled.

Usha kutty did not go down on all fours but she did plead, bleating pitifully in between loud sips.

My father stood up and placed a parcel wrapped inside a white hand towel on the table.

"Go on, open it."

Our family suffered an instant case of acute indifference.

"Morons," my father said. "Lack of curiosity could wipe out this entire race."

He took out a framed picture and offered it to my mother first.

"How much did it cost you?" was all our mother needed to know. I doubt she spent more than three seconds looking at it. But even after that short an exposure, I noticed how her face looked like a faultline was developing between her eyes.

I said, "Pass it to Usha kutty next."

Usha kutty studied the picture and then tossed it away, screaming.

It was my turn.

What I saw was a picture of my father. What I saw was also a picture of the lion from the Gir forest.

My father's head, adjacent to the lion's head.

The chin end of my father's head was attached to his body, as it should be.

But the scalp end of his head was inside the lion's open jaw.

It was hard to tell if the lion was ingesting my father's head or eliminating my father's head.

"Now that we are homeless," my mother said. "Your father is giving us some ideas on where we can move in next."

"Fool," my father shouted at my mother. "Just stop talking and start eating." He ladled spoonfuls of savories and rice and *payasam* onto her plate with both his hands.   "Eat, don't waste time talking. You are the one who wanted to go to Suri's and here we are, so eat, woman."

My mother sat still.

She must have imagined that meal so many times in her life that she probably couldn't tell the difference when it was actually there.

I saw her suddenly reach into her blouse and her hands groped inside her sari. Then she let out a loud yelp.

"I cannot find it," she said. "The money is gone."

"You have more caves in your body than Ajanta and Elora," father said. "Look carefully . . ."

"I can't find it," my mother cried.

"Can I have more rose milk?" my sister asked.

The server boy took it upon himself to bring her a refill. He pulled out a small pad, scribbled something with a pencil which he pulled out from behind his ear and left the bill under an untouched plate.

"The money for that picture?"

My mother looked at my father, who suddenly seemed more interested in the inspector's house.

That day I saw my mother sobbing into her hands but I knew soon, perhaps the next day, or the day after that, she would be off to the Zamindar's kitchen and cooking them the feast of their lives.

"Fool," my father said to her. "Do you want our daughter to get over her fear of lions? Or not?"

※　※　※

Only a few days later, we had to move into my aunt's house because we had no place else to go. My aunt said she had to put us up in her garage. But it was really her supply closet underneath an outside stairwell.

In return, my mother promised she would take my aunt's laundry to the river every day since water was scarce. Little Usha kutty was assigned the task of taking care of our niece, who was two years older than her. Usha kutty carried that brat around, cleaned after her, fed her and sang to her for two hours every night as she rocked her in a cradle large enough to hold a baby elephant.

And I continued to work at the harbor.

My father stopped talking.

All day and most nights, he sat on a mat next to a sack of cattle fodder and stared into a broken door.

"You'll see, all this will change for us soon, Appa," I said to cheer him up.

My father only nodded his head. It wasn't clear if he was chasing away a pesky fly or responding to my words.

I rode to the Zamindar's house to pick my mother up one evening.

The carnival music had died down and the grounds were emptying out. The stalls had been taken away. The lion had been moved to another location. Orphaned strings of lights swayed in the wind and the tents were being pulled down and packed away. Not one of the million people I had seen before was there and the fields looked unclothed and wretched.

I rode past the inspector's house and remembered the smell of the inspector's after-shave lotion. I thought about how his mouth was filled with betel nut so that he could barely talk, how the telephone pole on Pier Twelve next to Paris Corner always looked like it had cried red tears and how his suitcase with those crisp rupee notes cried out to me like a baby asking to be held.

It was late in the evening and the sun was bleeding into the ocean as I waited for my mother underneath a rain tree. I straddled the crossbar of my bicycle and thought about my father. About Usha kutty. The Kashmiri-Kanyakumari Express rolled by and my bicycle bell jingled without my permission.

Closing the door behind her, my mother rushed out of the Zamindar's house. She kept staring at the carnival procession leaving our town as she strode towards me. I thought about my mother too.

Over the years, she must have learned how to look at those carnival tents and the lights and the merry-making but only notice the empty grounds hiding underneath it all. That trusting emptiness was always there for her. Only the hoopla came and went.

"Any *ladoos* today, mother dear?" I asked when she hopped onto the crossbar.

"I'm not doing that sort of thing any more," she said tersely.

"No, you're right, Meena," I said, ashamed.

"Your father doesn't like it, you see," she said, looking very concerned for my father.

"Yes, you're right," I said. "You shouldn't have to do these things, Meena." It seemed obvious to me that there would come a time, when it would be the son's turn to stick his head inside a lion's mouth.

Weft of Dreams

> the animals, the animals
> staring from the end of the world
> — *W. S. Merwin*

In sleep, my hands fused into hooves.
I leaped, I gamboled over mountains —
my hardened feet free of pain.

My dream child, in smock of flax, sang to her pets —
a pangolin, black-footed ferrets, a margay cat.
How precious, the love of a child,

I thought, and hopped the paddock
to graze in her fold. Night trees
conjure visions of yearning —

animals — Or are these their
ghosts? — dance in hope
of one great turning.

Pangolin

Ball of pinecone scales,
coveted to ward off spells,
she rolls a shield around
her infant's life against hyenas
keen to dismember
this toothless mother.
Without her nightly work,
our world becomes an anthill.
Let no lion breach her belly,
let her tongue be daily
thick with termites, her
savannah face the sky.

Black-Footed Ferrets

As if decreed: No one
shall live underground,
tunnels have gone extinct
on prairies fit for wheat.
Worlds collapse beneath
the sod-buster, backhoe
renders burrowed denizens
scarcer still. The name
"weasel" speaks greed, but
who speaks of this glide
through earth, black-
masked and fleet?

Margay Cat

An angel that
never touches down —
born, fed, mated, high
in the canopy. Squirrel
of the cat world, with
eyes like saucers to find
monkeys in dark nooks.
How can paisley fur lie
at home on other backs?
Mine twitches, anxious —
Will he pounce on my
dream body? Goat hooves,

already cloven, split again,
again to grasp as hands —

Human, my sense of time so warped,
I empty the present in pennies of constant
change, scattered across a poisoned floor.

Child of my dreams, who loves each
glinting eye — delight couples
with desire to protect,

fright marries the will to serve —
before dawn she's immured
in the tower of sleep.

But what if she could teach, send some
wisdom out across the cold, a way
to learn to share this world?

Jorg Schmeisser, detail from color print, ink on hand-made paper

In a Ziploc

The poet from Haifa rushes in, hand out
as though she's brought something special
for her editor in Tel Aviv.
Who is she? I wonder —
this gray-haired interruption
who's come from the war zone
and can't wait to share.
"Look!" she says.
Not a manuscript this time,
but a Ziploc full of scraps
she's collected from the street:
pieces of the rocket
that just missed her house.

I gather my poems, suddenly small,
while hers fills the room, insistent as the sirens
that wail in the North.
Loud as exploding *Katyushas.*
All there,
exposed on her palm:
the raw, the unpolished.

After Bambi

Evening dampens into twilight
as I leave the cinema with my parents,
the night air calm
as the newscaster's voice
in the newsreel before the movie,
the gravelly voice saying
Hiroshima —
image of a grainy
black and white mushroom cloud,
and I look up at the winter stars sprinkled like salt,
and I wonder when my own sky will crack open
and level my own home,
and how I will find help
when my own body charcoals and splits,
and everyone around me
walks like blackened tree stumps.
Those who survived found a river
and submerged themselves.
We drive across the Mississippi,
moonlight shatters on the frozen surface.

How to Carry a Cross

—for John Dickinson

Scribe on my stone: Haunted by stories. It is terrifying
to be so moved, and I can cope none with *this* story—

John, father of my kindred, whose tales are a glowing
phosphorescence in the waters we tread, told me:

A quiet professor of his once opened himself, his reticence
banished by burden. Raised his first many years in Japan,

a loyal subject of The Crown, British intelligence
recruited him to recommend targets for a new weapon.

Their Second War criterion: population and industry.
Knowing friends there, his love of the region—certain

nothing would come of it, he suggested Nagasaki
and Hiroshima. Have you ever felt such burden?

Tell me how to show him the absurdity
of war, how to absolve one lone man of his special

guilt. Tell me you wouldn't shy from the impossible beauty
of him carrying a cross toward some distant hill.

The Osprey

Fog makes it easier to believe.
Wet, gangly trees

slope up from the water
bluegreen and graygreen

in half-written stanzas
disappearing by degrees,

the sun an idea only
where beach plums ripen

in the sky first
then on the branch,

seagrass saying *Wind*
saying *I and Thou*

and the osprey —
no more holy

than the water rat or cormorant
or beached kelp glistening

from last night's tempest —
no less holy

than the wood in this bench
than the stone in this man

the kingdom of the small
overwhelming the kingdom of the large —

from *this* and into *this*
the osprey breaks

with a fish in its talons —
and here is the world:

an osprey bearing a fish
and the word *fish*

over powerlines and marsh crabs
above swans and rotted docks

up to the platform on the utility pole
flapping three more times

to the shapes of hunger in the nest.

From the collection of the Editor

A Sort of Deadline

Yumiko jiggled the handle and thought, *break, broke, broken*. Was he in a bad mood today?

"Toilet's broke," she called, testing him. She waited, imagining the serrated tone he used to correct her English when he was upset. *BrokEN.*

He poked his head into the tiny room.

"What a surprise. What's wrong with it?"

"The flusher. It's not flushing." She wiggled the handle. Water sighed somewhere inside a pipe. It was an old-style squat toilet, a green porcelain basin sunk into the floor. Lou called it "the trough."

He scratched his beard. He'd stopped trimming it and these days it resembled a storm cloud about to burst. When they'd moved into this place after getting married, he'd taken care to shave every day. He was still teaching kids then, and some found the beard scary. Yumiko didn't care much for it either, but Lou only said, "When I'm around kids again, I'll shave."

She stood up and smiled at him, for the correction he had not made. "I guess I'll call Miura-san."

In the kitchen she shuffled through the papers on the bulletin board, mostly take-out menus. Underneath the flier for Tan-tan Men noodle house she glanced at the traditional two-year calendar—a housewarming gift from her mother. It was more almanac than calendar, full of symbols Yumiko did not understand. A few dates stood out, printed in burgundy; these her mother had taken care to circle with her own thick red marker. Auspicious days, meant for the events that indicated progress: weddings, job interviews, moves. Even, according to her mother, conception. The calendar had not been turned from its second month.

She finally found the landlord's number between pages of the CoCo Curry menu. Miura-san was not surprised at her complaint; the building was old, like all the others in Tainohama, and theirs wasn't the first toilet problem.

"It will be taken care of," he told her. "No more than a day. I hope you don't mind an inconvenience while the workers come by."

"Of course not," she said.

"As for your husband?" Miura-san always asked about Lou. "Is he still teaching at the grade school?"

"Actually, no. He's teaching business English now."

"I see. More money, I suppose." He continued gruffly, "Well then, I'll call the plumber. Expect them tomorrow."

"Thank you," she said, bowing slightly as she hung up. Lou mimicked her high-pitched formal Japanese, and bowed at her from across the room. She smiled, to encourage good humor on his part. But she kept the smile close-lipped; she'd noticed lately that big smiles pulled at her skin in such a way that her eyes almost disappeared. Was she getting old? Her eyes were her best feature, the color of weak barley tea, and strikingly light for a Japanese. When they'd first met, Lou had asked if she could really see out of them.

"He said they'll be here tomorrow to fix it," she said. "It'll take a couple of days." She had noticed Miura-san often underestimated the time things took.

"Hope it's not longer than that. I can only piss out the window for so long."

"If you did, Kobayashi-san probably won't even notice," Yumiko said. No matter what the weather, the old woman who lived below them never stepped outside without the protection of an umbrella.

But Lou didn't laugh. She saw him catch sight of the exposed calendar, its red circles like imploring eyes. She imagined its voice, a whisper: *Don't you want to know what the lucky days are this month? Come on, bring me up to date.* Yumiko looked out the window, where the sun was setting behind a network of rooftop antennas. She would not be the one to turn all those pages at once, pinching the months between her fingertips like food gone bad. She especially didn't want to see this, the eighth month, charted out. It marked their two-year wedding anniversary, which they'd celebrated by working late, and the weeklong *Obon* holiday, when dead family members were believed to visit the land of the living.

They both had the week off—Lou from teaching and Yumiko from a part-time job delivering telegrams—and Yumiko wondered how they would fill the time. Lou had balked at visiting her mom and dad. "All they'll talk about," he'd said, "is when we're going to wave the magic baby wand and turn them into grandparents."

She stared out the window. There would be a baby soon, she reasoned. He or she was just waiting for the right time to come.

Lou sighed deeply.

"Are you okay?" she asked.

"I'm fine," he said absently, gathering the scattered menus. He piled them all on top of the calendar, the tendon along his forearm popping out as he strained to pierce the clutter with a tack. Months ago, he would've organized the pile, thrown out duplicates or menus to places they never went. Now he just left it for her.

"I have to get to class," he said after he'd finished.

"Okay. Hey, how does *gyoza* sound for dinner?" It was a joke; the fried dumplings were the only thing she ever cooked, and almost always in the middle of the night.

"Wonderful," he said.

"Say hi to the beer ladies for me."

He nodded. Lou's last class of the week, Saturday night, was with a group of older housewives whose interest in English was a shallow cover for their real purpose: socializing away from home, where their newly-retired husbands lurked underfoot.

He slipped on his shoes. "See you later."

"See you," she said, and he disappeared.

"Oh, by the way," he called from the stairwell, "it's *brokEN*. If the toilet were *broke*, that would mean it's completely out of money. Not worth anything."

His footsteps faded. She opened the refrigerator and stared in. Suddenly, she couldn't remember what it was she'd wanted.

❊ ❊ ❊

Her first marriage hadn't worked out. They'd married out of college, but then he couldn't find a job, and then she got pregnant and he still couldn't find work, so they decided she would have an abortion. It wasn't such a big deal. People had abortions all the time; the local clinic took same-day appointments. Afterwards you visited a shrine and bought a *jizou*, a small cement figurine representing a soul that had not yet found its way to Earth. The statues stayed in the shrine, lined up like dolls in a department store. The priests blessed them every morning.

Less than a year later, he'd come home from a temp job at a waste disposal plant and dropped the envelope from the travel agent on the table. He was going back to Okinawa, he said. He had family there. She had felt many things, among them relief, as if some great disaster had been averted. Anything, she believed, could be tolerated if it was straightforward; at least you knew where you stood. It was the in-between area that terrified her, so that night, she watched him pack with a feeling approximating fondness, or pride, and marveled that perhaps they'd had more in common than she'd thought.

❊ ❊ ❊

That night, Yumiko woke at 3 a.m. and couldn't get back to sleep. She went to the kitchen, as was her habit. First she chopped vegetables: cabbage, *nira*, green onion, garlic, ginger. She salted the cabbage and set it aside. Getting the dough right took time, and she added the water drop by drop—make it too wet, and the insides fell out. Her mother had told her once that the dough should feel like an earlobe. She poked and rolled and kneaded with her fingertips, palms, the backs of her hands. Sometimes she imagined it *was* an ear she was creating, part of an incomplete sculpture. She pressed the water from the cabbage and laid out small circles of dough upon which she arranged vegetables and morsels of pork with the fastidiousness of a surgeon. Then she folded the skin upon itself, crimped the edges together six times, and dropped the resulting crescent into a pan of hot sesame oil. It was at this stage that she usually woke Lou up; the sudden scream of the oil jolted him from sleep. But that night, he slept through it.

She'd come the night before, and the night before that. Three nights in a row was a first. Things were coming to a head, she thought. Lately she'd had a feeling that something was behind her, lying in wait in the shadows, some change that would only show its face when it was too late to stop it. It was not the first time.

It was the season, perhaps. She'd married Lou over two years ago, a month before the *Obon* holidays. Last year *Obon* had been a week of parties, drinking with friends, karaoke and fried treats in the park. They'd attended a short ceremony at the shrine with her family, honored her dead grandparents by lighting incense, and, as an afterthought, said a prayer for the soul of Yumiko's unborn baby. Afterwards she and Lou had met up with friends and danced at a nightclub until the sun came up.

This year, their friends were traveling, or had babies of their own. Her parents had moved back to her mother's hometown in Nagano. Lou had come home from work on edge that night, and they had argued again about whether to visit them over the holiday week.

"I really don't want to face your parents this year," Lou said.

"But what else will we do? It's tradition."

"Yeah, I know what the tradition is. But can't we take a year off? Tell them we're taking a trip or something."

"But we're not."

"Maybe we should. Maybe it would do us good. We haven't gone anywhere since our honeymoon."

"I know. It would be nice," Yumiko reflected. "But hotels will all be booked by now."

"I just don't think we need to be thinking about the dead this year. Or at least, I don't need to. You seemed to enjoy it fine last year at the shrine."

"*Eh? Nanda rou!* What are you talking about?"

"You know what I'm talking about."

She was quiet. Finally, she said, "You know, it was never alive."

"What?"

"It's not dead. It was never alive."

He said nothing.

"It's just waiting for the right time. You know that's what we believe."

"I just don't see why you have to rub it in my face every year that someone else got you pregnant and it was just an...*inconvenience.*"

"I told you we weren't ready! Should I have stayed with him instead? What do you want me to do?"

He just stared.

"A year or two isn't that long," she continued. "We should be more patient. It isn't easy."

"You made a baby for him easily enough."

She'd walked out then, and wandered the streets for over an hour, fuming. Yet she could see his point, and that was what hurt the most. The doctor could find no explanation for their difficulty. She wanted more than anything to be a mother, to bear his child, and no matter what the doctor said to the contrary, she still wondered if her abortion had hurt their chances.

When she returned his eyes were red. He apologized so sincerely that she gave in, and told him they could stay home for the holiday. They went to bed after that, and though it appeared things had been resolved, a gap separated their futon, and they fell asleep before either moved to close the space.

❊ ❊ ❊

The next morning, the doorbell rang at eight. Yumiko woke up, confused. Who would come by so early on a Sunday?

Before she could rouse herself, there came a pounding on the door. From outside someone called, "Plumbing!"

He's certainly getting an early start, she thought, pulling on her robe. She hoped that meant they'd be done early. Then they could just sleep through everything.

She smoothed her hair and opened the door.

"Mornin,'" A chubby man smelling of cigarettes nodded at her and looked inside as if waiting for the man of the house to appear. When he did not, the man shrugged and said, "Here for the toilet," and stepped over the shoes heaped in the entranceway.

Yumiko backed away, rubbing her eyes. "Um—"

"Checkin' out old toilet today, doing some testing on the pipes," he said. Two men walked in behind him, one older than her grandfather and another not over fifteen, both lugging toolboxes. They stood in their boots, in her kitchen, and looked around.

"*Gyoza*, yum!" The grandpa stalked over to the stove. "Do you mind?" he asked, his hand inches above the plate.

"Oh! No, not at all! Please, please, eat up."

"This thing is heavy," the teenager whined, and set his toolbox on the floor.

"So here we go," the chubby man said. "Bathroom's here?" He pointed at the door.

"Yes, that's right," Yumiko said, and took a deep breath. "Is this, um...excuse me, but what are you doing exactly?"

"New toilet's going in. But first we gotta take out the old one, maybe replace some pipes. Might be a few days."

"New toilet? I don't believe we . . . ."

"Just following orders," he said, and grabbed a *gyoza* before disappearing into the bathroom.

"I see," she said, staring at the bedroom wall.

She returned to Lou, who was awake.

"Let's get out of the house today," she said.

They went to the beach. It was uncomfortably warm already, and Lou's hair puffed up in the humidity. They arrived early enough to get a prime spot but Lou, as always, led her to a rocky corner near the breakwater. He was the kind of man that, given first choice of desserts, would choose the most undesirable one, just so that he wouldn't have to share it. He avoided crowds if at all possible. Once, when they'd first met, she'd asked him why he'd settled in such an overpopulated, and foreign, country. "To escape my family," he'd joked, and when she pressed him seriously he'd finally responded that he enjoyed the challenge. As she bobbed among the waves, studying him in his corner, she reflected that her husband seemed to enjoy a certain *lack* of challenge, as well.

They'd met in an Osaka art gallery showcasing life-sized puppets. He was thirty-one; she twenty-seven. She'd been hunkered on the floor before a toe-tapping marionette with clenched fists, sketching, when Lou had appeared next to the puppet, tapping his toe and clenching his fists. He seemed to take no notice of her, as if he too was impatient and his stopping there was merely coincidence.

She looked up and laughed. He said, in stumbling Japanese, "Are you a puppet too?"

They talked all afternoon, then over dinner. Her English had been better than his Japanese, and still was, thanks to the two years after college she'd spent in Chicago, studying sculpture. When it turned out that neither of them actually lived in Osaka, but an hour east and only four train stops apart, they called it fate. A year later, they got married and moved closer to the seaside, dingy as it was. They wanted their children to grow up smelling the ocean.

The beach did get crowded eventually; the crowd grew to such a size that even their sad patch of sand was not spared, and they drove home. On the ride back, Yumiko found herself hoping that the workers would still be there, pounding and chattering, anything to fill the silence that these days lay between them at night like a third, invisible person.

✢ ✢ ✢

The first thing she noticed when she walked in was the smell. It was like someone had re-routed the neighborhood sewer line directly through the kitchen.

"What the —" Lou began. He stood in the doorway, open-mouthed.

Tools littered the kitchen floor so thoroughly that there was no way to reach the refrigerator without kicking something. A puddle sat defiantly in the bathroom doorway, and as they stood in silence, a bead of water fell into it with a *plop!*

"You've got to be fucking kidding me," Lou finally said. He picked his way to the bathroom door.

"They took out the toilet!" he called.

"Yeah," Yumiko said slowly, "they mentioned they were putting a new one in."

"You knew about this?"

She shrugged. "Only since this morning. It will take a little longer, but won't it be nice to have a normal, you know . . . throne?"

"It would be nicer to not have my house torn apart."

Voices came from the stairwell. The crew appeared and grunted greetings. The boy sucked on a cigarette, focusing on its glowing end. The other two stood in the kitchen and continued the discussion they'd apparently been having outside, about whether or not the Japanese Pro Baseball League ought to allow foreign players.

Lou interrupted them. *"Excuse me,"* he said. *"But we don't allow smoking in the house."*

Yumiko could tell that it was not his request that fazed them, but his decent Japanese. She felt a surge of pride. The boy raised his eyebrows, nodded, and took one last drag before stepping to the door and flipping the cigarette outside. "Eku-scuze me," he said brightly.

Lou went outside and stepped on the butt, pulverizing it beneath his flip-flop.

Guess who gets to clean that stain off the walkway, Yumiko thought.

The only thing more annoying to Lou than smokers were the *bosozoku,* "noise gangs" of bored teens who removed the mufflers from their motorbikes and raced up and down side streets, shattering the silence at odd hours of the night. Once, last month, when a group had gathered in the parking lot next door, Lou had jumped out of bed and climbed onto the roof with a carton of eggs. After some confusion and yelling, the roar of engines faded; smiling in the dark, she thought to herself, a Japanese man would never have done that.

In bed a few minutes later, he was triumphant. He liked taking care of her, he said. Then, as he pushed his way inside her, he'd whispered, "Our baby won't be like those kids."

She joined him in the stairwell, where he was nudging the cigarette butt off the landing with his toe.

"This is crap. How can we live like this? This week is *Obon*, they'll be off every other day. Why'd they even bother starting now?"

"Let's go back out. Take a walk."

"And why the hell do we need a new toilet? The old one was fine."

Yumiko sighed. "I think Miura-san thought he was doing something nice for you."

Lou rolled his eyes.

"Well, he's putting in a Western-style toilet. He probably thinks he's doing you a favor."

"I never asked for a Western-style toilet."

"I know."

"I don't need favors like this. It's not like because I'm American, I need a special potty."

"I know. But it will be nice, for me too, most places these days don't even use—"

"And he'll expect me to be so grateful," Lou went on, and bowed deeply, throwing his arms out to his sides. "Yes, I'm so indebted to you, there are people flooding my apartment and messing up the kitchen so much we can't even use it and reeking up the place with smoke!"

Yumiko was quiet. Finally, she said, "Let's just try to make the best of it."

"Sure, wonderful. How about giving them our bedroom, so they can just sleep here?"

"Well, you know, we could still go to my parents' place. They really...what's that face for?" He was staring at the metal ladder that led to the roof, as if suddenly enlightened.

Slowly, he said, "No. We're definitely staying here."

"Oh boy. You have an idea."

He smiled. "We'll move onto the roof."

"What?"

He was nodding to himself. "That's it. It's perfect! We'll bring the futons up, some books, your art stuff, whatever we want. It never rains in August, and it's warm enough to sleep outside. The perfect vacation."

"You're kidding," she said, but he was already inside, throwing open the sliding doors that hid the *futon*. She looked doubtfully at the ladder, then back into the apartment. On the bulletin board she could see the calendar, its gilded edges poking out beneath the pile of menus. Lou, so obviously pleased, lumbered toward her with an armload of pillows. She reflected on the portability of their lifestyle, how even the marital bed was easily hidden away behind doors that slid soundlessly, like ghosts.

❖ ❖ ❖

She woke up staring into the pink-dappled sky. Lou slept facing away from her, his body curled around a pillow. For once, he did not snore.

The air was calm, heavy on her face yet soothingly cool, like a washcloth. She did not move, and breathed only shallowly. She imagined she was floating in a bubble that might pop at any moment. No matter what happened during the rest of the day, she could always close her eyes and recall this world, where she was the only one awake, where her only duty was to inhale the dewy air.

And then a voice: "*Kirei, da ne?*"

Beautiful, isn't it?

So he was awake after all. It had taken her a moment to identify Lou's voice — as if it could have been anyone else, up there. But he spoke Japanese with her so rarely these days that other possibilities had entered her mind first. Her ex-husband, for one.

"*Un,*" she acknowledged.

She heard him rustling the plastic wrap that covered a plate of leftover *gyoza*.

"*Mmm. Nothing like a dumpling at sunrise.*"

A moment later, he rolled over. "*What shall we do today? The beach? An art museum?"*

She watched the clouds. The way he put the past behind him amazed her, this capacity for acting like nothing had been, or could ever be, wrong.

"Or maybe . . . hey, how do you say 'rooftop nudist colony' in Japanese?"

She sat up and ran her fingers through the tangled hair that fell halfway down her back. He was in a good mood, at least. "The beach again sounds nice. And we could shower there. My hair is gross."

"I had this dream," he said, reaching up and fingering a lock of her hair. "You had your hair in braids. Have you ever done it that way?"

She shrugged. "When I was in high school, maybe."

He sat up and began to divide her hair into sections. "Did I ever tell you how glad I am you don't dye your hair?"

"Yes. All the time."

"I don't know what I'm doing," he said. "Do you just wind it around like this?" He swizzled two pieces together.

"Here." She took the pieces and smoothed them between her hands. "Like this. You make three sections. *Ichi, ni, san. Mitsu ami, dan-dan."* Her fingers moved nimbly as she recited the rhyme. *"The boy chases the girl, captures her beneath him, the third comes between, like this, and from then on they are —"* she paused, then left off the last line of the grade-school chant, which played on in her head: *"a happy family woven together."*

"Ta da!" she said instead, holding the finished braid out to him like an offering. He took it.

"Amazing how girls can do that to their own hair," he said. "Like it's an instinct or something."

She said nothing.

He took her hand. "It's our own little world up here. Do you like it?"

She nodded. She *did* like it. "It's like we're flying on a magic carpet. Or pioneers on the frontier."

"The *gyoza* settlement," he said, plucking another dumpling from the plate. He hesitated, then put it back and instead lay down, pulling her with him. The sky was brightening; a mile away at the town park the trees on Shiroyama stood silhouetted against it, like sentries keeping a polite distance.

❖ ❖ ❖

The seaside was not as crowded as usual, probably because many people had left town. This put Lou in a carefree, happy mood, and when they returned home, hungry and sun-baked, the kitchenful of workers did not dent his good spirits. Something was happening, something that made Yumiko believe it was possible, healthy even, to put the past away and enjoy what you had.

They agreed immediately on a restaurant, a ramen place known all over the prefecture for its pork broth, and draped themselves leisurely in a back booth. Lou filled her in on the beer ladies. Kimiko, a woman of sixty who had climbed Mt. Fuji every year since she was in college, was back after a two-week illness. She'd been bedridden, she told them, and her husband, for the first time in his life, had had to prepare their meals.

"The guy didn't know where to find the toaster," Lou told her, his eyes wide. "So he cooked the bread right on the stove burner!"

Yumiko laughed. "Oh God. Lucky for me you're American."

"Lucky for both of us there are so many restaurants nearby."

After dinner they walked along the river. On Friday, the boardwalk would be packed with people dancing, drinking, and lighting lanterns; booths squeezed in along the riverside would sell everything from fried squid on a stick to giant pet crickets. But now they were alone on the dark walkway. Even the river seemed motionless, and the only sound they heard was the one-car train that brought tourists to and from the seaside. Though it was too late for the beach, the train still ran, shuttling nothing but dead air.

In the silence, she felt she was expanding, as if the bustle of daily life had been holding her true self at bay. It was like shedding an irksome undergarment; life had been girdling her.

She felt this no more strongly than back on the roof, with its elevation above the roads and storefronts, its face open only to the sky. Everything in her sight yet seen by nothing, this was how she felt she belonged. There was something nourishing about it that reminded her of her delivery job. Taking care of other people's important documents, she felt powerful, yet invisible; people paid her no more attention than they would a mailbox. Recently she had begun to read the telegrams: business contracts, directions to questionable "bathhouses," progressively desperate love letters from a certain manager to a secretary at another company, who, as far as Yumiko could tell, never responded. She felt no guilt in reading but rather was heartened by the flow of it all. It seemed evidence that the world was full of momentum; that somewhere, progress was being made.

It seemed as though progress had seeped into her life as well. After Lou had fallen asleep, she was overcome by such goodwill that she crept down the ladder and made *gyoza* for the workers. It was the first time in months that she had prepared it for any reason other than filling time. Gleeful exclamations woke her the next morning when the men arrived. She blinked happily, gazed at the pale sky, and fell back to sleep.

Over the next few days, she and Lou developed a routine: mornings spent on the beach, the scorching afternoons whiled away at the oddly named Café Sometimes. The café was a lucky find, open during the holiday week and stocked with American board games Yumiko remembered from her days in Chicago: Connect Four, Monopoly, Life. A "Grand Opening" banner hung above the door. Always the sole customers, they basked in the smile of the owner, who fussed over them as if *they* were the new things.

In the evenings they ate out or had a picnic on the roof. Yumiko brought up some clay and created a makeshift studio; the little objects she fashioned by moonlight—cups, saucers, vases—she left out to bake in the next day's sun. And after the crew left—for they had come every day, despite the national holidays—she made a fresh batch of *gyoza*. Since that first time, she had always arrived in the kitchen to find the path to the stove and refrigerator cleared.

She threw up on Friday night. It came upon her suddenly, while she was adding water to a batch of *gyoza* dough, and she barely managed to step over to the sink in time. While she leaned heaving over the basin, excitement burst through her chest and set her body tingling. She was not one to vomit for nothing. Other than one night of heavy drinking, the last time she'd thrown up was when she was pregnant.

She washed her face with dish soap, rinsed out the sink, and sank to the floor. She breathed deeply, wondering what to do. There was a convenience store nearby where she could buy a pregnancy test. But Lou was due back any minute, and would wonder about the half-made dumplings. He'd be sure to ask where she'd gone, and she didn't want to raise his hopes in case it was a false alarm. She had disappointed him enough.

As she rose to continue her baking, she heard him coming up the stairs. A moment later, he opened the door a sliver and spoke through the crack.

"Yumi, come up in five minutes, okay? I have a little surprise."

"Okay," she replied. The last time he'd said that, he'd asked her to marry him.

She retrieved her makeup kit from the bathroom, which was still crowded with tools and pieces of pipe. The new toilet, complete with heated seat ring and button-activated bidet, sat in the shower, waiting.

In the kitchen, she applied blush to her reflection in the toaster. She brushed her hair and drank some water. Did she look too pale? She walked outside to the ladder, leaving the unfinished *gyoza* behind.

She had so masterfully avoided discussing the evening's plans that she'd forgotten to think about them herself. Friday, of course, was the final day of Obon, when the spirits returned home, the day of the riverside festival when candle-lit paper lanterns crowded the water. Once, as a child, she had seen one of the floating lanterns catch fire. The paper was so thin that the entire lantern seemed to disappear in a single flash. Her father had called it a bad omen. Secretly, though, she had found the boldness pleasing, surrounded as it was by such uniformity.

She climbed up the ladder. She hoped his surprise wouldn't interfere with a trip down to the river. She didn't consider herself religious. She knew that a few miles down, low-level government workers would fish out the lanterns and throw them away before they reached the sea. But some rituals were just a part of her, the way Americans all seemed to go to Super Bowl parties even if they didn't care for football. They could piece together a meal from the food booths, drink some beer, and watch the fireworks.

But when she reached the top, she gasped. Lou sat surrounded by candles, cross-legged, among dishes of glistening food and three bottles of red wine. His head and face were completely shaved.

She took a deep breath, and let her gaze fall on the candles behind him. The flames looked hardened; the air was so still she imagined there was no wind left on the planet; it had blown its last gust and given up.

"The fireworks are starting soon," he said, reaching for her. "We'll have the best view in the city."

She stared at the back of his hand. It was lightly furred, a quality she'd always loved. Now it looked like the hand of a stranger.

"Your hair," she said.

"It got to be too much. So I ducked over to work while you were cooking and plugged in the shaver. I thought I'd start over." He rubbed his shiny head and grinned. "What do you think?"

"I don't know what to say," she began. "I mean, it's…clean."

He made a face.

"No, I like it! I just…all this…I thought we'd go down to the river tonight. You know, for the lanterns."

He rubbed his head. "But we're having such a good time up here. I thought we could just celebrate our own way this year."

"Celebrate what?"

"Um…being together? Being a family?"

"Can't we celebrate that at the river?"

Lou gestured at the food. "No need."

"Can we just please do the one thing I want to do? Isn't it enough that we didn't go see my parents?"

"Well we didn't go see my family, either," Lou said, picking at a plate of fried chicken. "And this is one of the few times I get a whole week off."

She sighed. "You don't even like your family."

"Fuck, Yumi, I just want my own family, my own traditions. Something new. I left home to get away from obligations and now I have more than I started with."

Yumiko walked to the edge of the roof, her heart in knots. When she spoke she imagined the words falling to the alley below.

"Maybe you should go home then."

He laughed quietly. "Don't make this about you. I'm not your ex."

To the west, a small white firework tested the air. *Snap.*

"It is about me. Come on. Me and my stupid womb."

He shook his head. She had never realized how irregular the

skull was, what imperfections hair concealed.

"I thought we could start over up here, somehow."

They were silent for a while.

Finally he sighed and said, "I didn't want this week to end."

And she knew that he was referring to more than the time off work, the breaking of old routines, the gleams of hope they'd both felt in just forgetting it all. To him, this was a sort of deadline.

"Lou." The fireworks were popping regularly now, blasting through the blackness like wounds.

Her tears were pooling already and his expression, when he turned to look at her, made her want to sink to the ground. There was little that needed be said. But she asked anyway, because she saw in his face that he expected it.

She did not ask: Is a baby more important to you than I am?

She did not ask: Will you leave me if I'm not pregnant?

She clenched her fists and asked, *"Dono gurai?"*

How long do I have?

He sighed, and lay down on his back. For a moment his eyes reflected a green firework in miniature, then he blinked and a tear spilled down his cheek. A breeze slid past Yumiko's face, carrying the harsh scent of gunpowder. Some of the candles went out. The air registered cool on her nose and forehead, flesh so hot that she knew then that something was burning away inside her, like a lantern thrown off-kilter at the wrong instant.

Une Pomme de Discorde

*—French idiom referring to the apple Paris gives
Venus, arousing the hatred of Juno and Minerva*

When I want sweetness, I prepare
to slice it fine, keep the seeds.

I have it. I give it to her.
The equation is simple.

Small and probably red, it poses
on the palm of Venus like a gem.

By giving it to her, I have
not given it to anyone else.

Who holds the apple changes
another with desire and guilt.

Whom do Juno and Minerva hate?
Themselves, for being empty-handed.

She, the egg of love, the dust
of skin, lifts it now and bites.

What Is the Spirit of Thermopylae in the Modern Age?

Days after I watched *300*, a movie about the battle of Thermopylae,
I thought of my father, Yeh-yeh,
who was, in his own way, a kind of warrior —
a journalist who never flinched before the horrors of
the Pacific Theatre in World War II —
how he never uttered a word of complaint
when they restrained him to the hospital bed here,
when they injected him with three times the normal dose of tranquilizer
but failed to sedate him to force him
into an MRI machine where he didn't want to go,
when they fed him through a tube in his nose,
when they cut off his left leg,
how even when he asked to go home
and was still walking, eating
and we said not yet,
he didn't argue with his sons
but suffered silently
waiting patiently for relief
by the armies of reason
that never came.

Again

Yeh-yeh is 92,
Nai-nai 81.
In the 57th year of their marriage,
Yeh-yeh fell, went into the hospital,
told Nai-nai this might be the end for him.
Before his second stroke
Nai-nai said to Yeh-yeh, after she died
she wanted to come back as a man because
she was tired of being a woman.
Yeh-yeh said fine,
he would come back as a woman
so they could meet and marry again.

There's No Getting Around Grief

for Chang Jen-chung, 1911-2005

We tried so hard to burn Yeh-yeh
according to Nai-nai's wishes.
We dressed him in his best black suit.
We bought him an extra-large white shirt
from Filene's on 79th and Broadway
because he had put on weight
under Nai-nai's care in the last year
even though he was dying.
We stuffed $50,000 of paper money
in his pockets because his whole life
he was afraid of being poor.
We gave him peanuts in a paper bag
that his granddaughter, Amy,
had tied together with a golden ribbon
because he loved peanuts
and walnuts because his grandson, William,
and his granddaughter, Beverly,
remembered how he liked to crack
walnuts and eat them.
We gave him a transistor radio
so he could listen to the news and weather
and fall asleep to the sound of human voices
as he did every night in life.
We put the poem, "Again," in his jacket pocket
so he could remember his promise to Nai-nai.
We stuffed a pillow in the empty
leg of his left trouser
where his leg had been.
We put a small pillow under his stroke-immobilized left arm
so that it could rest easily.
We put shoes, his best penny loafers, on both his feet —
the one that was there
and the one that wasn't.
We put photos of Beijing in the pocket of his jacket
so that he could find his way back home,

two small clay soldiers at his shoulders to guard him
and two small clay horses at his feet to carry him
wherever he wanted to go.
We covered him with the red fleece blanket
his grandchildren had given him
so he wouldn't be cold.
We placed a small hand towel by his head
with six small blue roses that Nai-nai had embroidered by hand all day.
But in the transfer from the New York Mortuary to the Ortiz Funeral Home,
a pillowcase that Nai-nai made for Yeh-yeh was removed
and Yeh-yeh had to leave this world
with his head on a bare pillow, just like
Nai-nai's father when he was buried
by her brothers in China during World War II.
Twenty years ago, when she finally saw a photo of her father's burial,
she demanded to know from her brothers
why they hadn't even put a pillowcase under his head.
She asked them what was wrong with them?
What were they thinking?
Said to them that had she been there,
she would have taken off her underpants
and sewn a pillowcase for their father.
For twenty years, she had never spoken to her brothers
because they had buried their father without a pillowcase.
Now,
she would have to remember for the rest of her life
that we burned Yeh-yeh without a pillowcase under his head.

As my wife and I stood outside the car,
at the shopping center
behind the crematorium in Old Bridge, N.J.,
I said to my wife,
I said to the air—
"There's no getting around grief."

Canning Apricots

The first day I bled,
it was in the sweat of summer.
Aunt Eva helped me
make my own rags.

Then we washed and hung
the laundry out. Eva clamped
three pins between her teeth
and snapped the wet sheets.

I stuck my face in one to sniff it.
Eva jerked me back, pinched
a knot in my shoulder. *Girl, listen.*
You marry—and this is what you do:

You lean back in bed. You
close your eyes. You pretend
it's summer. You pretend
you're canning apricots.

Aunt Eva turned from me.
She stamped through the dry grass
towards her peeling white house
with the empty basket on her hip.

Lesson from The North Shore

Like upright skeletons, Minnesota birches
line up between Lake Superior and me.
They're not fat like my oaks and locusts
back home in North Carolina. Many have
had their heads snapped off, leaving
jagged wrists pinned to a hard blue sky,
the silver skin spotted and peeling.
I'm only a seasonal, but locals say this is
the way it goes—dying from the top down.

In Season: Pomegranate Glosa

But Persephone is not this poem's source
although the pomegranate, swelled with garnet seeds
inside its secret membrane, may mislead you.
At birth a woman has 1 to 2 million eggs
tucked away. A nest egg. There they hide, glowing like jewels
in the sweet full-moon bellies of young girls
beloved by Artemis. Not the other one.

The fruit's sweet seeds line the held half
in impossible curves, must be plucked out,
must pop between teeth, taut with juice.
A woman learns to trust she holds all possibility
in her ovaries. By puberty she will have lost
the moon. It will own her, push and pull.

Artemis guards the threshold, demands blood
for spilled blood, her crescent sickle moon harvests
300,000 in a natural process known as atresia.
Persephone, appalled, says little, eats less.

But this is not about her. Half her seeds
already gone, she can only sit in darkness
and weep at poetry. Half a pomegranate eaten
myself, I'm mooning over the fact that,
with every cycle, 1,000 more will die
until we have no children, like Artemis with no light
of her own, the old moon in the new moon's arms.

Fetal Skeleton, Mütter Museum

Frail fetus, laid out as if filleted,
your dainty fish bones behind track-lit glass
aswim in ultraviolet. Fine specimen,
you choke my throat, unmade while barely made
(no way to know if you were lad or lass,
although the latter sounds more like lament).
I could pick my teeth with you, could bait
your thin ribs and catch more with every cast.
White script, you are both human document
and diminished thing which pricks my pen:
Write this.

Post-Caffeine

We don't speak of ourselves
with the same colored eyes
any more,

or with a honeyed sweetness
on the tongue. We taste
our bodies with the caress

of a hand,
a surreptitious foray
into the dark

of fingers touching fingers.
The smell of coffee
thickens.

This place,
built between hills,
reminds me

of a woman's pelvis.
On a cold day
it becomes the focal point

of brightness, of expressions
of deep growth,
a moist reek

of beginnings
people first up in the morning,
pushing out faces

blinking in the winter,
the frost on wires,
blowing small thermal eruptions

from pink mouths.
I lick in the caffeine
as if I'd just been kissed.

Being born each day
helps
in the unravelling of trees,

in the forcing apart of dark skies.
I take to the road
shoving back

the crisply-cut hedges,
the glow-worm curtains. And
there's always the latecomers,

the stragglers
drifting home to their holes
after dark.

The morning is a flawless
brilliance of waking
and a jewelled dampness

mirrors the appearance of others.
I seem to be living
in the transparent softness

of a giant lens
far from the way
we discovered ourselves

night-struck, but surviving —
the contusions of dreams
slowly healing.

The Plants

She is making love to them
Caressing their leaves
Giving them the gentle attention that I have not gotten for a while

When I go out to meet her
The sun creeps, cowers behind the shoulders of soil
Shaming me

And the water hides in the hose
And she stands there
Gaping

"Now look what you've done!
Harry, what you have to chase away the water for?
And for the love of God what have you done to the sun?"
I skulk right back in
Double-checking our locked and secured cabinets,
The boudoir
The drawers

And the sun stretches out
And the water is a kid again
Mimicking Sponge Bob
Triumphant
In the playground, she is pushing him on a swing
Laughing the laugh of children
She gets back down to business, giving all of her attention
To those plants

from *House Not Made with Hands*

Learning from Experts

> Starchy vegetables cloud
> stock and should never be
> used.
> —*Henri-Paul Pellaprat*

Put down that potato. You are silly with your college
stew, your *mélange*, your *ratatouille*. It is time to go
beyond the chop, the toss, the cover-and-cook-till-done.
You are capable of more refinement. Look to your stock:
fond blanc ordinaire, brown stocks one and two, *court
bouillon*. Today we start with bones and pure water
attended to the boil. Be a fanatic; skim for impurities;
add herbs you've grown—Italian parsley, thyme, a leaf
from your laurel tree. Adjust heat for the coolest of
seductions. Heed the French: keep your liquid at a
tremble. Three hours. Four. It must evaporate slowly,
like lust from a hot affair. Now, strain through cheesecloth
as fine as a communion veil. Balance the flavors on your
tongue. Now, you are ready to begin.

The Priest Reads from St. Paul

Uniformed girl
I felt his voice
on something

never touched

> *So being affectionately desirous of you*

winglike   rustling
golden cloth of thick-nubbed silk
across my shouders

desirous

> *My dearly beloved and longed for*

a doll the only thing I'd held

now this

> *Greet all the brethren with a holy kiss*

my lips to my hand
damp to dry   barely salt

testing for holy

something grew
added layers

something

launched

> *Beloved   beloved   beloved*

I flew

a falcon
not yet taught
to find the falconer's arm.

Henry Philologizes

Once again the Discordians are nagging him
like midges over his beloved river on a calm
summer afternoon. He wonders why
they shun the clear flowing stream to seek
the cesspool of town. Or why—here he stops to pick
a clod the harrow knocked out of the field—
the words we use for the earth we plant our feet on,
our seed in, to grow and nourish us arise
from filth and defecation.
For *soil,* friend Webster tells us, is moral defilement,
corruption, excrement—as well as
the unconsolidated upper layer of the earth's
mantle. And *dirt* from the Old English *dritan,*
to defecate. He raises the earth to his nose,
then advances his tongue to it. It is sweet
with the things that have grown in it: the sunburst of corn,
the red sweetness of maple, the butter of the nut.
How eagerly it opens to life; how
secretly it guards root and seed.
He sees its fine dust covers his hand,
blackens beneath his nails. In town the Discordians
scrub and shine vainly trying to shield
themselves, little reckoning they are washing away
their next meal. Instead they busy themselves
assigning value by means of names and never
watch the poppy unfurl its tissue wings
that bruise from the very ecstasy of beauty—to fall,
to rot and melt, to give back to the earth.
Striding across the wordless field he plunges
into its manurey blackness, carefully tamping
himself down, and listens for the hum of cells
at work within, swelling, dividing, pressing
till root pricks and tears itself into speech.

In the Time of Falling Away

The autumnal nature
of this late spring weather
brings darkness to mind
nights too crisp for a summer quilt
rain more than the earth can drink in.

And there are the tent caterpillars
in the apple tree
making lace of the foliage
leaving only the veins
full of sap
with no flesh to nourish.

Hold me tight, dearest,
before it gets too late
and fading like Eurydice
I cannot reach your hand.

Bulkheads

There are dozens of ways to 360°.
It's mostly in the hips

he promises.
We never know when

the ocean might surprise us.
What if an arm or two gets tangled up

in harpoon line?
What if suddenly

it's time to paddle upside down?
My leukemic friend and kayak mentor

is counting on remission, a year or more
including time

to teach me how to roll
like an Inuit.

Because of him I've added bulkheads
fore and aft, watertight,

silicon caulk, and lots of it.
He wants us to go out and play in the surf,

capsize for fun, for the hell of it.
He can spin like a dolphin,

float like a cork, regulate
his angular momentum.

He knows when
to get nowhere fast and how

on a whim
to return to where he started.

There's no reason not to trust him.

In the office of the Director of the Balance Center

next to Audiology
on a desk near a model of the inner ear

a dozen paperweights are waiting.
She picks one up and makes it snow to demonstrate

the way the brain knows where the head is heading.
From the desktop of her laptop she double-clicks a film clip

of two eyes gazing to the left and ticking like a watch —
clockwise when standing, counter-clockwise when supine —

since disembarking from a cruise on the Aegean.
Her finger tracks the voyage of the otoliths, calcite crystals,

bone and stone now old enough to float. On a related subject
the 3rd auditory ossicle is as small as "In God" on a dime,

if you've ever read a dime. Hearing and balance, two sides of one coin,
depend on endolymph in motion to activate the 8th or auditory nerve.

Vertigo can be loud as a tunnel or quiet as a cricket,
a *silver cricket* the patient explains.

Lunge

This young woman with two leashed dogs
lunging up and down our street

is normal. Her younger brother isn't.
They live around the corner.

They used to ride the bus with our kids.
They swim where we swim.

She never acts embarrassed
by the noise he makes when splashed.

A happy noise, I suppose.
Her dogs are small and round,

vicious terriers, overfed.
For years there was one, now

she's training its replacement.
I have no idea what it's like

to have a brother who can't speak
or feel like going for a walk

or plunging in the deep end.
The old dog is what gets to me,

the taut leash, the hot tongue.

Father

> If your right eye causes you to sin
> tear it out and throw it away.
> —*Matthew 5:29*

You have grown quiet. In the silence let me
tell you the story. In this telling I am fontanel
and mead, spoke and tender. It begins
with wine in small bottles that roll
under the bed and pills as blue as peacock
or hyacinth. They sing me into a nap before I have even
swallowed them. Then, of course, the ambulance,
the neighbors watching from their front doors.
In this story I am stricture and boiler
and breath as shallow as Cypress. Stay with me.
They watch as I unhook my bra, the bald
knowing. They listen to my heart. They whisper
in my right ear while the map of human anatomy becomes
a map of South America becomes a map of 9 AM.
They feed me charcoal through a straw and send me by taxi
home to sleep. Sepia draws me at the bed.
Sepia is the color of the walls. I do not want to go on.
You know as well as I do
that separate is the word for apart
and prepare. We both know that confession
does not necessitate forgiveness. A promise was broken.
A lie told. But, in my defense, how do I know
your voice from my own?

Monograph

Listen carefully. You will sing again.
With the blue pill, your hands
may swell. You may
feel thinner than you are,
a mackle may appear. Remember,
I repeat myself so you are sure
to understand. Remember,
I have given you a story
so that you may know motion towards force,
a needle threaded with wire,
a hem unblinking. Listen,
even the throat of a cardinal contains
darkness. The green pill will go down easily
despite its size, even two parallel
lines meet if you watch them
recede. I am that I am
singing smoke. Listen,
even your darkness knows.

The Shell

Martin Wyss had not planned to carve for the dead. He wanted to carve horses and bears and ducks — hooves so hard they could run, fur so soft the chest could rise and fall, wings so strong they could fly. Martin knew he was meant to uncover what was hidden in wood, wanted to pull life from it just as Michelangelo had grabbed David's marble hands and tugged. Michelangelo loved David because he found him in stone, and for the same reason Martin loved the ducks he discovered preening their oaken feathers.

Sometimes, late at night in his garage workshop, Martin was sure he could hear sleepy quacks from the wooden beaks and tired pawing from the hooves of deer. But in spite of his attainment of the near-perfect duck, Martin had to work part-time at a hardware store because his art barely sold. Perhaps a dog here or there at art shows, a fawn from time to time, but most people smiled and nodded and walked by.

His aunt requested the first casket. She was seventy and a chain smoker, knew he was hard up for money, so she asked him to carve a four-foot-high hollow teacup with a hinged lid. It was as if she knew in six more months she would need to curl inside. His teary uncle paid Martin handsomely. A librarian aunt asked for a casket shaped like a row of books. A mechanic uncle wanted a toolbox coffin. It did not take long for word of Martin's artistry to spread like a plague. Calls came from eight states, orders for a windmill, a racecar, a violin case, all big and with hinged tops. It was too popular, Martin thought, the idea that in death one could lie in what one had loved. He quit the hardware store to carve full-time, but each coffin was labor-intensive, made just enough to pay for his food, mortgage, car loan, and buy materials for the next casket.

You must be so happy now, his friends said, able to carve for a living.

Martin shrugged. He still saw deer and bear sitting in the wood, wanted to carve life but had to serve those who sat nervously at its edge, people who were wilting. Usually he had clients to his workshop twice—once to view his work and place an order, and again for a casket fitting, since it was only proper to make sure he had sized them correctly. Martin kept these appointments to a polite fifteen minutes, averted his eyes when his clients rested their wizened legs inside the coffin and either pronounced it comfortable or a little too tight. By the time they left, Martin's fingers had started aching and his knuckles appeared slightly knobbed.

He had the earthy build of a carver, short thick arms and legs and a sturdy torso, but Martin knew even the healthiest of bodies only allowed for so much time, so much completed work. Around the perimeter of his garage, wooden ducks watched him in sympathy.

❀ ❀ ❀

Odessa Crouch wanted to be buried in a big purple scallop shell. She was sixty-one and on disability, a recently retired legal secretary at Hummer, Hummer, and Huller. The law firm was downtown, next to the pink marble art museum. Odessa wandered the museum's halls during her lunch hour, strolling past Egyptian mummies and Roman sarcophagi, browsing the gift shop and flipping through poster-sized prints. Botticelli's "Birth of Venus" was her favorite, the goddess rising from the sea in her oversized shell. A lovely way to be born. A lovely way to die. It had been fifteen years since Odessa's body had started hurting, really hurting, and now it always tried to curl in on itself. Her hands, her feet, her arms, her legs, wanted to wind in tight spirals close to her torso, condense into a ball.

Odessa had felt useful at work before pain cut her off. She'd organized legal papers and made phone calls about divorces, custody battles, alimony, and DUI. She was someone who helped sort things out. When Odessa's husband had left her for an older woman ten years ago, she got free legal services. Her two daughters were grown by then, had demanding babies of their own, and Odessa managed to get fifty-five percent of everything because her lawyers were vultures and her husband a wimp. Half of her possessions were willed to her two daughters and three grandchildren, the other half were supposed to be sold upon her death and the proceeds given to the museum. Odessa believed in art and free admission.

She'd heard of Martin Wyss's caskets from a friend of a friend whose aunt had been buried in one shaped like a giant candy bar. The box was white pine but everyone at the funeral swore they smelled chocolate. Odessa wondered if, when she was buried in her scallop shell, people would smell the sea.

When Odessa called Martin to inquire about coffin prices she thought his voice was too high, too weary. Odessa bit her lip. She wanted someone who carved caskets to sound like God.

I'm thinking of dying sometime soon, said Odessa. I want a casket shaped like a shell.

What kind of shell? said Martin. Abalone? Conch? Clam?

Scallop, said Odessa. Like Venus.

She wanted to be laid out in the fetal position. Now her wretched spine ached and made her hobble through the grocery store hunchbacked, but she thought that in death the curve would be beautiful, even graceful, once it did not mean pain. She wanted Martin to react to her saying she was thinking of dying soon. Instead he asked where she lived.

You should probably come to my workshop, he said. It's not too far, maybe an hour's drive, and you could see a few of my works, decide if it's what you really want.

Odessa agreed even though she didn't drive much anymore, didn't do much of anything anymore without a lot of ibuprofen and sometimes Vicodin on top of her monthly cortisone shots. The pain flowed through her like blood, up her fingers to her arms, down her back to her legs and knees and toes. She'd worked as long as she could at the law firm, longer than her aching body wanted to allow, until the afternoon Mr. Huller brought her a cup of coffee and said quietly that perhaps it was time to take a rest. She was a hard worker, he said, and she'd earned a break after thirty-five years with the firm. Odessa was certain her arms never hurt more than when she had to clean out her desk. The heat of that pain never left. Odessa hated the way her fingers arched into claws when she didn't take her medication. She hated the way her legs ached in the morning, the way her veins popped out blue against the peach of her skin. She hated the way her feet felt like she was walking on popcorn kernels. Her insides had been replaced, muscle by muscle and bone by bone, with someone else's aching interior, and deceitfully covered with her own skin.

Odessa took a triple dose of ibuprofen on the day she drove to meet Martin. Her doctor said it would harm her stomach eventually. Odessa didn't care, just wanted to keep her body at bay. She focused on the shell, imagined it was just a pen flick away, the writing of one small check, and she'd figure out the rest from there.

Martin Wyss was one of the most disappointing men she had ever met. Despite his too-weary voice, Odessa had still hoped for a man who looked like he'd been peeled off the ceiling of the Sistine Chapel. Martin was five feet tall if that, had a bit of a paunch, was balding slightly, had arms thick as tree trunks, and not enough wrinkles to be over forty. He was the sort of man she'd expect to come and repair her sink. Martin showed her his garage workroom. It smelled not of wood but of dead forests, burned things. One casket was in progress on the wooden bench, a seven-foot-long ice cream cone wide enough for a human body.

You realize that in a shell they couldn't lay you out to your full height, said Martin.

Of course, said Odessa. She was five-foot-nine, taller than he was. Odessa explained her idea for the fetal position.

When do you plan on dying? said Martin.

Odessa wrinkled her nose. One month, she said.

If you could hold off for one more, he said, make it two, I would be finished by then. Have to get this one done, you know. He nodded at the cone.

Of course, Odessa said again. She wrote him a check, a down payment on her shell.

I guess that's about it, said Martin, folding the check in half and slipping it in his pocket.

You don't need to ask me anything else? said Odessa. Measure me?

I have a good eye for size, said Martin, tapping his head with a sad finger. I'll remember.

On the drive home, to take her mind off the pain searing back into her fingers, Odessa reconsidered the possible means of her demise. She thought about jumping off a bridge or tall building, but that would be rather disgusting, and they'd have to dredge her body or put pieces of her in the shell. She didn't want to send workmen home retching tales to their wives. There was always a gun or a knife, but those were violent, involved too much blood, and she did want to be presentable when tucked in her shell. As much as she hated her body, she figured that it might as well look halfway decent once it stopped hurting. Poison would taste bad, and there was always the chance she'd vomit it up. She could take sleeping pills, but what if someone found her and took her to get her stomach pumped, or what if she didn't take enough?

Odessa gritted her teeth. She wasn't going to simply lie on her couch and wait for death, wanted to attend to these matters while she still could, but she finally decided, as she usually did, to put off the question of how she would die until later. The means itself was not that important. What mattered was the shell.

❖ ❖ ❖

After Odessa left, Martin kept sanding the ice-cream-cone coffin. It was for a man who'd owned three sweet shops and was not a small fellow. He had heart disease and the doctors didn't give him long. Martin smoothed a sheet of four-hundred-grit sandpaper along the wood grain. Nearly done. It was not a bad sculpture, but all of his caskets felt unnatural, like they were forced out of the wood. They did not flow with the same grace as his animals. He was usually pleased enough with the finished coffin because his customers were happy and that mattered a great deal to him, but carving a casket was not truly satisfying. He opened a can of stain, Satin Woodberry, mixed it with a stirring stick, and began to rub it on the cone with a rag. The wood turned the color of graham crackers.

He thought of Odessa and her thin knobbed frame. Hers was a body that made one uncomfortably aware of bones and joints. Even though he was not old, he felt the pressure of age, the urge to find things in wood while his hands could still firmly grip the chisel. Martin worried about his body hurting, hardening, paining with life as Odessa surely pained.

He figured she'd probably look better once she passed. Most people did. It was the in-between time that was upsetting, when people had bodies that were withering or oozing and not much could be done about it. Such had been the case with his mother and his tea-loving aunt, who both died in nursing homes. Martin went to visit his aunt once, his mother twice. They were barely more than skeletons, had machines that breathed for them, fed them, removed waste from their bowels. They blinked at Martin sadly and touched his hand. Their skin smelled peculiar and was slightly sticky, had been claimed by odors and textures no amount of washing could remove. After the initial visits Martin stayed home and worked on the coffins—his aunt's teacup, his mother's pink pump.

His mother loved shoes, fancy ones. She had beautiful feet, ones that looked like they belonged to a forty-year-old even when she was seventy-eight and needed a walker to shuffle around her house. She did so in gold beaded slippers, red sequined sandals, low fuchsia heels, or lavender flats with daisies embroidered along the side. Her neighbors called Martin on the day they found her collapsed on the kitchen floor. The doctors told Martin her insides were failing. The first time he visited his mother, Martin took all her shoes to the nursing home and lined them up on bookshelves along her wall so she could see them from her bed. The second time he visited, the exquisite definition of her bones was too much for him to bear.

While she lay between too-sterile white sheets, he knelt in his garage, glued five thousand magenta sequins on the outside of the pump, and remembered his mother at fifty-five when she was plump and brown-haired and smelled of cinnamon. Martin could not explain why, but the shoe had emerged as naturally as his animal carvings, as if that block of wood had only ever wanted to be a very large high-heeled pump.

Martin made a point to go to all of the funerals where his work was displayed. Even though he was ambivalent about some of his caskets, he felt a duty as the artist to attend the memorials as there were few other places where his art was praised. The deceased always looked pleasant, wore fancy clothes as if ready for a concert or dinner party. His mother and his aunt had been tucked snug in their coffins in nice dresses, their faces made up, their hair neatly permed. Both of them seemed to have gained a little weight and there was a hint of color to their cheeks as if they had just come from a brisk walk. It was reassuring how their bodies had been restored, how they were now caught in a moment of pristine order. Martin could make himself imagine they had died like that.

❖ ❖ ❖

Martin called Odessa after four weeks, earlier than she had expected. He wanted her to come look at the shell and check the fit.

Odessa still hadn't figured out how she was going to kill herself, but hoped Martin might have some knowledge on the subject of death.

What's the best way to die? said Odessa after she pulled into his driveway and got out of her car.

I don't do consulting, he said.

I'll pay you extra, she said.

I'm really not an authority on the matter, Martin said.

He turned and started walking to his workshop.

But you see a lot of dead people, Odessa said, hobbling after him on her sore feet.

When people come to me, Martin said, they usually aren't in a situation where they can choose how they're going to die.

Nobody opts to go out early? said Odessa.

If they have plans they don't share them with me, said Martin. I'm just an artistic advisor. Sometimes they ask me what they should wear after the fact.

He opened the door to his workshop.

What about how not to die? she said.

Drunk and penniless in an alley, he said.

I hadn't considered that, she said.

Don't, he said.

The shell was on his worktable, lovely and cream-colored and satin smooth, perhaps five feet long and five feet wide and two-and-a-half feet high when the halves were together.

Martin said, I still have to sand the inside a bit and screw on the hinge plates, but I figured you should try it so I know if I need to carve out more room.

Odessa's legs were paining, she'd forgotten her pills in the car, but she grimaced only slightly when he helped her up onto the sturdy worktable, lifted the top off the shell. The hollow inside still bore slight grooves from Martin's chiseling tools, but despite the roughness Odessa curled herself into a dreamy fetal position. It was perfect.

I like it very much, she said.

Martin stood by the table.

Looks good, he said after a moment. You can stand up now.

No, said Odessa because the shell seemed to make her elbows and knees ache less. It would hurt to get out. In the shell her insides felt different, softer.

✿ ✿ ✿

Martin chewed on his bottom lip for a moment, then for what he judged to be five moments.

You have to go. I need to keep working on the shell, he said.

I like it in here, said Odessa. I don't want to get out yet.

Martin said, I told you, it's not done.

You have to work on it right now? said Odessa.

Martin didn't say anything, stood there a little longer. He'd progressed on the shell more quickly than expected, found once he started working on the scallop it became an obsession. The shell mesmerized him with its contours, the grooves in its smooth surface. Martin studied scallops before he began working, loved how the sea creatures could secrete a hard casing around their bodies, how they lived out the entirety of their lives in the shell.

When he started to carve he found the scallop was already there in the wood, smelling of sea, waiting to be released. The shell was not merely a box. It was a creature. He lavished the outside with sandpaper, regretted having to hollow it out, wanted to carve the scallop itself. It was what belonged there, not a middle-aged woman.

Martin wanted to line the shell in cream satin, paint the whole thing periwinkle, imagine a three-foot-wide scallop could rest there. He wanted to float it in his bathtub and watch the scallop's massive foot poke out between the two wooden shell halves, flawless and petal-smooth, to explore the ceramic contours of its new home.

But Martin was afraid of Odessa, didn't like looking at her for very long. Partly out of anxiety and partly out of hunger he decided to be nice, have an early lunch and give her a few more minutes in the shell. In the kitchen Martin lingered over his ham sandwich and the newspaper, waited a full hour before returning to the garage to confront Odessa.

Time to get out, said Martin.

No, said Odessa, I'm staying here.

✿ ✿ ✿

She had been thinking about the shell every day for a month. There was ample time to do so since most of her hours were spent watching television and trying to alleviate her pain through learning about gardening and cooking and needlework. She kept forty bags of peas in her freezer, pulled twenty out each morning after breakfast and put them all over her body while she lay on the couch. There was still pain but it was numb pain that made it easier to separate her mind from her body. Around two in the afternoon she put the twenty defrosted bags of peas back in the freezer and took out the remaining twenty bags of frozen peas, repeated the process.

The wooden shell felt warm and cool, even more soothing than frozen peas. When she concentrated she thought it was rocking her back and forth.

Martin said, Don't you need to go to the bathroom or eat?

I'm going to die here, said Odessa.

❖ ❖ ❖

Martin flexed his fingers, wanted to protect his shell, haul the scallop to the water where it belonged. He thought Odessa's face had turned a shade paler since she'd arrived, but he could not be left in his garage with the beautiful shell and the husk of a woman. He would not be able to control the drool threading from her mouth, the loosening of her bowels. Usually when Martin carved he did not feel his body, it became part of the wood. He was the wood. If there was an ache in his elbow or a sliver in his thumb it was overlooked, unimportant. Nothing existed but the next stroke of the chisel. Odessa, like his other clients, made him aware of the fragility of his lungs, the stiffness of his fingers, the twinge in his lower back.

You can't die in the shell, Martin said. You'll ruin the aesthetic. People are supposed to look nice for their funerals. If you starve there, all covered with shit, it's not going to be pretty.

❖ ❖ ❖

Odessa wrinkled her nose and shifted her legs slightly in the scallop. Martin had a point. If she stayed in the shell to die she might look more like a baglady than like Venus. Not that she'd entertained the thought of looking like Venus. Perhaps Venus's aunt or first-grade teacher. Presentable. But in the shell her body curled happily, able to rest as it wanted.

❧ ❧ ❧

I'll call the police, Martin said, his words echoing on the concrete floor. They'll come and dump you out.

Odessa coughed. Let them, she said.

Martin paused.

If you don't get out, I won't sell you the shell, he said.

You have to, she said. I gave you an advance.

No contract was signed, he said. I'll give back your money and keep the shell myself.

This was a wonderful and an awful idea, and one he'd been considering since Odessa arrived and he realized how badly he wanted the shell. If he didn't sell it he might not have enough in his account to pay for his mortgage and food and car loan, but he also knew Odessa couldn't die in his garage and guessed she had the power to do so.

Odessa was quiet for a moment.

Bring my pills from the car, she said.

He found her purse. He found her keys. He found a small bottle of pills on the passenger seat, gave Odessa the four she requested along with a glass of water and a half-hour to get ready.

❧ ❧ ❧

Odessa knew she needed something to drink. Even more importantly, she believed Martin when he said he would not sell her the shell.

Pain surged as soon as she stepped out of the scallop. She lost that sweet peace with her body. When she went to the bathroom she had diarrhea. Martin was good enough to make her some mint tea, though, and when she held the warm mug her fingers hurt a little less.

The shell could be finished now, she said. Just tie it to the top of my car and I'll take it home and pay you in full. It would be less work for you.

Odessa knew that if she had the shell, if she could lie inside it without pain, it wouldn't matter so much if she lived or died.

❀ ❀ ❀

No, Martin said. It isn't done. I have to paint it.

He couldn't part with the shell, didn't know if he could find another piece of wood that would contain a shell so lovely. Better to go into debt while he made Odessa another scallop. He wanted this one.

Odessa finished drinking her tea. They walked back outside to Martin's garage and stood by the worktable.

If you're not going to let me take it home yet, Odessa said, let me get back inside. Just for a little while. I don't ache as much now. I'll be able to get out.

You need to go home, Martin said.

Odessa put both of her hands on the lip of the shell. Her fingers were thin as crab legs.

Please, said Odessa.

Her nails dug into the wood. Martin grabbed the other side of the shell and pulled. The shell was heavy, moved a few inches across the wooden tabletop. Odessa didn't pull back, her arms were not strong, but her fingers were set, her muscles locked.

You're supposed to have more compassion for the dying, she said.

Dying people aren't supposed to be belligerent, he said. They're supposed to be sickly and meek.

Forget meek, she said. If I really wanted to I'd make myself drop dead right here, and then what would you do?

Martin stared down at the floor and imagined Odessa's insides leaking out.

I'll give you twenty percent extra if you let me get back inside, she said. Just for a moment or two. I promise.

Martin gritted his teeth but nodded. He'd carve a second shell and charge her more for that one.

Two more minutes in the shell, he said. That's all.

Odessa asked if he could put the top on the shell first, attach the hinges.

Martin wrinkled his nose.

It'll be harder to finish the inside and paint it, he said, but eventually he agreed because he was eager to see the shell together, too. He hurried through the half-hour it took to position and screw on both brass hinge plates. When he was done, Martin raised and lowered the top half several times before helping Odessa back onto the table.

❊ ❊ ❊

Odessa curled herself inside the shell. It still felt warm.

Close it for a minute, she said.

Martin obliged, lowered the top half gently onto the bottom.

Odessa heard him count to five before opening it again.

No, she said, I mean a minute.

Martin rolled his eyes but closed the shell again. It was dark and warm and Odessa heard him whispering one-one thousand, two-one thousand, three-one thousand. She heard the sea. Her joints loosened and she felt floaty, as if she was immersed in a pool of water that wasn't wet. Too soon the crack of light at the opening of the shell widened to an annoying brightness.

Okay, that's it, Martin said, tapping the side of the shell.

No, she said.

If I have to push the shell off the table to get you out, said Martin, I will.

It might break, said Odessa.

Get out, said Martin.

She didn't.

❊ ❊ ❊

It was too much. Odessa's skin smelled medicinal. Martin imagined her hands caught in a clench, her face becoming paler and harder, her chest ceasing to rise even the tiniest bit, her cheeks caving in. There could be no dead things in his shell.

❊ ❊ ❊

Odessa heard a door open and close. After a couple of minutes she heard it a second time. Then she felt the shell start to move. She still didn't believe him, figured it must be an empty threat until the scallop slid off the edge of the table, dumped Odessa onto the couch cushions Martin had arranged on the garage floor. The shell gaped over Odessa like a huge open mouth, just missed hitting her arm. Odessa started sobbing.

You didn't give me much choice, Martin said quietly as Odessa lay on the cushions.

The smell of the sea filled her nostrils, soothed her slightly so her eyes did not burn so much. Martin walked around the table and eased the shell off Odessa, centered it on one of the couch cushions.

She stopped crying. Her face relaxed. Her bones ceased to ache. Odessa rolled to her stomach and planted her hands on the floor, stood up. Something around her body had been lost, a sense of grounding, gravity. She felt a release in her legs, her hips, her spine, sweet and sudden. The smell of the sea was potent. New strength surged in her arms. Odessa knew that for at least a few minutes she could be powerful outside the shell. She pictured herself carrying the scallop to her car, driving home with the trunk cracked open slightly.

When she grasped the edge of the shell with her thin fingers, she saw her veins were growing brighter, nearly glowing through her skin. The shell slid more easily than she had expected, off the cushions, onto the concrete garage floor. Martin gaped at her.

Odessa pulled it down the driveway, paused for a moment when she felt her arms ache, but a second wave of strength rolled through her body, and she kept going.

I'll send a check, she called to Martin.

※ ※ ※

Martin could not move. He winced at the sound of the wooden shell grating against the concrete driveway, but shoving it off the table with Odessa inside had drained him. He could not chase her. As Odessa lugged the giant scallop to her car, her power was mythic. But when she was halfway there, Martin noticed her pace beginning to slow. Her body bowed over, closer to the ground, but she kept lumbering backwards, even as her fingers loosened incrementally. He knew what was coming. The slow motion tumbling forward as if into a pool of water. But not just yet. Odessa pulled the scallop along.

For a moment the driveway dissolved, the harsh cement went blue, the shell floated along and Martin envisioned the barest shimmer of a young woman's gold hair, hands covering herself in modesty, then he saw the second figure, the silver gray of an old woman's hair, her nakedness without apology as she tugged the shell through the waves.

In the Macula

Many violences came to them,
all at once, and now they can't stop

their vision. It hums and grows.
Ultraviolet is a terrible thing

to see. A pear's light is the same
as her hand's, and he doesn't trust

himself to know what to bite.
They shut the lights, stay in bed.

A book spine inks her breast
like a tumor. He takes walks

when he can't avoid his anger
at how so little can bruise her

so badly. Outside, the people
are hooded and gray, but he knows,

no matter what, she is always
the soft yellow of petals.

He goes home and they shut
the blinds against the light, and curl —

first one the hand and one the pear,
and then the other way around.

A Microcosm

Mammals rose from dinosaurs,
Renaissance from the Middle Ages,
Beethoven's Fifth from his deafness.

The perennials under a juniper in my yard
need more sunlight; the weak plants
sensitive to rainfall. In their roots

the energy stored grows foliage
until dry days arrive. Year after year,
they barely survive. This year

the weather is right.
Small white flowers bloom.
Orange-red Chinese lanterns.

john urban

chose me
for lunch each day
instead of the flamer
who begged him.

we never ate
but walked east lansing
or i held him
on his bike.

The Paleontologist's Lover

What are you searching for, there among the rubble,
Lost among those bones?

Take off your helmet. It is no good to scrabble in the dust.
Willy-nilly, this way, that.

Frenzy never discovered what was lost. How have we
Uncovered any truth from clay?

A dental pick, a fairy wand. A horse-hair blush brush,
Stolen, from the makeup aisle of some convenience store.

Arm yourself with blunt tools, my darling. Lay down
Your armor. Enter battle unafraid.

The Paleontologist to His Lover

Here in this hot bone-bed, I am searching for you,
Sweat-dripped, tracing tracks in sandstone with my fingertips.

No locus, no center, no skeleton complete.
Though I have dug for hours,

I cannot find the joinings of your bones.
I am missing vertebrae, mandible, your right ring finger.

Try and try,
I cannot make you whole.

Penobscot Voices: Kikukus

Padjo Sussup

Mother died in childbirth.
1902. Passamaquoddy—
      from Peter Dana Point.
      Mud-doc-mig-goog
On Big Lake.
Near Princeton. No doctors.
Convulsions. died.
Just-like-that.
Grandmother. It was lucky.
Had her last baby two days later.
Nursed us both. The smallpox came.
Three years and gone.
I was all she had.

Grew up blessed.

And grandmother,
A young woman, still.
Made baskets. We'd
Peddle them in her
Horse and wagon. House
To house. Then came the
Diphtheria, Scarlet Fever, the
Whooping Cough. We didn't know.
Grandmother was smart. Made me
Chew calamus root. *Kikukus,*
We call it. Reek strong.
Side of my face
Get numb. Hers too. Probably

Day, maybe more,
Before we taste
Food again.

Kikukuß.

Means "cure thyself."

Never caught a thing.
And grandmother,

she died old.

Glenn Herbert Davis, photograph

Carried Away

In the afternoons, Binky and I read love letters. They are not to or from us—though we are dear, dear friends and roommates, too. The letters come, one each day, to the apartment where we've lived for two months in this, the biggest of cities. We are new here and hopeful. We are not yet thirty. We are tampering with the U.S. Mail.

When the water boils, we hold a sealed envelope in the steam and count to ten. Then we slide a scissor blade, softly, under the flap. We squeeze into the only chair, an heirloom from my grandmother, and take turns reading out loud. The cat sleeps in a spotlight of sun.

Dearest Michael, reads Binky. *Long-Lost. Remember when I slipped in the shower and dragged the curtain with me. I made a clumsy nude, but you found the whole thing erotic!*

Such letters are for Michael, the previous tenant, from Diane, his ex, a self-proclaimed *fallen woman.*

You liked me like that, on the bathroom floor, Binky reads, and says, "It's no better than porn. It's lamer. We should finish unpacking."

❉ ❉ ❉

"Hush it!" Binky yells at the pigeons.

They are hurling themselves against the window, bleating sadly. Sugar stalks them, mewing and lashing her tail.

"They look cold," I say.

"They have feathers. That's what feathers are for."

We drink wine from plastic cups because the glasses are still in boxes.

"Coming out?" she asks, pouring me thirds.

Binky's divorce went through in September. For weeks, she dragged me with her to the too-young bars in the meatpacking district. Twenty-five minutes on the train, forty-five on the platform, waiting. Now I tell her: go, have fun. She can leave with whomever she wants—the square-jawed playboy, the professor in cowboy boots, the eighteen-year-old drummer who says he plays "prog."

In two months, I've gone home with two men—thin, sad whisky drinkers. Both were overly grateful in bed. *Tell me what you want,* they said. I slept over. I drank coffee in their studio apartments and wrote down phone numbers that weren't mine and let them kiss me hopefully against the doorframe. They had the same Klimt print in their bathrooms.

Binky always comes home before sunrise. She may or may not wash up before crawling into my bed; hers is buried in laundry. I'm never asleep. *Rub my feet,* she whispers. I hold her in my arms and press my fingers to her temples, and she tells me about her men, every detail. When I wake up, she's snoring. Asleep, she smells like milk just before it goes sour, milk you have to smell again and again to convince yourself it's still good. She is so much taller than me. When we spoon, she sticks out, her head and her long, long legs; I cannot contain her.

When I say I'm staying in, she makes a show of being offended, glides out the door sideways, slams it. Then I hear her running back up the stairs.

"We forgot to get the mail," she says, waving a small lilac envelope.

✿　✿　✿

For the first week or two, we put Diane's letters in a pile. We really meant to send them on, to take them to the post office. But the sheer number did us in. Or was it the lavender smell, the careful cursive rendering of our address? Was it Binky's still-recent divorce? My dwindling savings? Our unemployment? A consequential boredom and despair? We agreed only that resistance was futile.

When we read those first two or three in hot succession, we slumped in the chair afterwards, exhausted. Our jaws ached as if from kissing. They were long, digressive letters.

"I'd forgive her," I said, just as Binky was saying, "I'd have her arrested."

"Arrest *us,*" I said, "for this federal offense."

She said, "The guy should forward his mail."

Through the window, while we read, we can see someone's laundry hanging on a line: underwear of gargantuan size, sometimes with ruffles. We can make out the words on one billboard:

Él está viniendo! Binky and I try to guess what this means. There is no context, just bright red letters on a white backdrop, something in Spanish. At night, the words remain, lit from below by spotlights. *I'll look it up,* we promise each other, but we don't.

I dreamed of our view, writes Diane, *the one from the living room window. The fat woman's underpants were scrolling by. I dreamed I was the highway below. I dreamed I was the view itself.*

❊   ❊   ❊

The letters reveal that Diane has *strayed,* and more than once. Sometimes she calls Michael *prudish, Victorian. Monogamy,* she writes, *is for swans. Swans. I want to snap their necks!* Other times, her promise is fidelity forever. *Let's be two birds. Please say there is no one else.* Diane lived here, too, before the straying. Besides sprawling on our bathroom floor, she dropped an air conditioner out the alley-side windows (its remains confirm the story); she painted a fake fire in the decorative fireplace (the interior paint does seem thicker); she loved how tall and wide my bedroom windows were (and are), and once she unlocked the metal guard and stood there, six stories above the street, offering to hurl herself out of them, if that's what would make Michael happy (of this, there is no evidence).

❊   ❊   ❊

"Where are you going?" I ask Binky.

"To work," she says. "Remember? I'm doing that sales thing."

"You're handing out fliers," I say, but she's already out the door.

When the phone rings, I'm hoping it might be the temp agency. Before I can swallow and give my most lovely hello, there is a woman's voice.

"Michael, don't hang up."

A seductress in her dressing gown, smoking: that's what the voice was like.

"I'm sorry," I say. "I'm not Michael."

"Who the hell—" she says.

I hang up. There was a response I should have given, something stock that slipped my mind like easy things sometimes do. As in: how to spell "iron," whether the sun rises in the east or west, what the capital of Pennsylvania really is.

Later, Binky picks up the ringing phone. She stands with one foot cocked like a flamingo's: "You must have the wrong number."

Of course, she is right; that's what you say no matter what.

❖ ❖ ❖

Today I say, "Hello?" and Diane says, "Look, I know where you live."

❖ ❖ ❖

Where we live is the northernmost point of Manhattan, where everyone — excepting us — speaks Spanish. The rent is cheap. Our apartment is six flights up, stairs only. We've got hardwood floors, French doors, stained glass half-moons above the windows. The bathroom ceiling narrows to a point. From downtown, we *take the A train*, seven stops past *Sugar Hill way up in Harlem*. We're no more than fifteen miles from the suburban high school Binky and I once attended, and where I was (until a few months ago when funding got slashed) director of the chorus and the predominantly white gospel choir.

The A pauses in the tunnel between Dyckman and 207th, the end of the line, to wait for a signal: for one stretch, the same track serves trains in both directions. In that moment when everything is still, we look around the train for Diane. Once we were almost sure. But tonight I'm alone, and there are no other women; the lights flicker a little but hold. Four young men are nodding across the car and approach, ask politely for my wallet. It's the kind of crime where you catch yourself saying, "you're welcome."

They nod, pulling out bills (I have eight ones, nothing else), leaving the cards. One man's fingers touch mine as he hands the wallet back. His head bobs, something tugs at his mouth — and he seems just like that student, the boy who always came late to choir rehearsal. He'd slink up the risers while the rest of the tenors — their mouths making happy, punctual O's — warmed up. His voice, joining the others, was something to hear.

"The fuck you smiling at?" the boy says, and I realize I should be afraid. But the train moves again; the boy turns away.

❀ ❀ ❀

"I wish someone would mug me," says Binky from under my comforter. "This city is a Starbucks Christmas card."

Binky was too recently together, isn't used to being separate. I've grown into separateness, grown used to taking up all of my bed.

"Why are we awake?" she asks.

I have an interview at ten, for an office job. The company publishes music textbooks K-12. *We have a sheet music series*, the human resources woman said, *and 401K*. So I put on my interview lipstick and smile and shoes. Letters are scattered across the living room floor, the breakfast bar in the kitchen. Sugar chases one into the bathroom.

❀ ❀ ❀

I'm wearing Binky's good luck blazer and the sleeves are too long. The building is a glass tower on the burial ground of Penn Station. On the billboards around it are giants in sunglasses, fake smoke billowing from their cigarettes.

The interview is in a dimly lit conference room, no windows. People's mouths move quickly, without sound or stopping. My ears need desperately to pop. We must be underwater, or at a high altitude where you have to bake things longer. Of course I can read lips, but what is that prior experience to my greatest weakness, where I see myself in five years? I am muddled in acronyms and nonsense words, in disjointed rhythms, accents, patterns. "GOSPEL choir. You're JEWISH, right? That MUST have BEEN an experience!" *Inflections*, Diane writes, *make me itchy. I'm sleeping with someone new and he calls me DI-ane, emphasis on DIE.*

I don't know when to speak, when to listen. My résumé, printed on expensive white paper—paper with a texture—is like a clue. I touch my fingertips to it again and again. That sprite of an assistant pokes her head in to see if we'd like anything. Her lips say: collated, stapled, ready. *At work*, Diane writes, *the printer prints your name. The copier copies it. The people wear masks of your face to meetings*. What a face it must be! The interviewers look at me and nod and smile as if everything is normal, as if I am doing beautifully. I shake their hands and they say they'll be in touch and the elevator doors yawn into the lobby.

❊ ❊ ❊

Binky doesn't come back all night long. I lie awake, reminding myself to breathe.

❊ ❊ ❊

Half a block from our building is a mom-and-pop diner without a name, just a big sign that reads: COFFEE ❊ DELICIOUS BUNS. A couple fights in the booth next to ours. *What is this rubber doing in your pants? Baby, I told you. These aren't my pants!*

Binky tells me she's met someone.

"It's not serious," she says, like a promise. "But it's good. My man friend says he can get us some work; he owns a restaurant in Tribeca."

I want to reach across the table and push the bangs from her face; I want to see how it was with him.

"Not this one," she says, pulling all of her hair into a ponytail.

I point at a woman by the window; she's alone and drinking a strawberry milkshake.

"Could that be her?" I say. "The letter said she *hasn't gone far*. There's nowhere else for brunch above 190ᵗʰ."

Binky pays the bill, then says we should actually see the Cloisters while we live up here. We climb our way there, through winding paths in the woods; the vegetation is wilder and thicker than Central Park's, and there are fewer people. We move aside to let the homeless man with his pack of dogs go by. Just off the path, lampposts lie on the ground like fallen persons, their glass heads cracked or missing.

Binky gets bored after fifteen minutes, but I stay. *Sometimes*, Diane writes, *I see you on the street, but then it's really someone else. I can see that when we start talking. Sometimes I take you home anyway, and it's nice, pretending like that for a while.*

In the museum's herb garden, I wait for the blonde in the feathery coat and tall boots to turn from the view and face me. A

woman in sunglasses cries by the unicorn tapestries. The security
guard places one hand on her arm, and I stand transfixed: such
kindness! But she is saying, sternly, *don't touch these.* It's Diane who
turns away, who feels the pain, who scolds others for feeling it. It's
Diane who writes: *Why do the bad things, small, outweigh the numberless
good? Stop weeping into your navel. Is that how the saying goes?*

❀ ❀ ❀

Binky dashes in the door, shedding her scarf but not her
boots; she strides across the letters.

"Where do you go," I ask her, "all day, all night?"

"You're quoting her," she warns.

She means Diane, of course, Diane in three months' worth of
letters. Binky's man friend got her a job as a waitress. Her hours
are midnight to six AM. Some days she temps in an office, and the
time between is for *amour*, as she puts it.

"You quote her, too," I say.

But Binky says that's just a saying, something for anyone.
My prospective employers say, *no-no-no*, in roundabout ways, in
tongues. The answering machine is a garble of their collective
words; it forces my head underwater to hear them.

"You're so sensitive," Binky says, kissing the top of my head.

"You're so happy."

She says I should call that temp place again. Or go back to
school.

"What does that mean, *go back to school*?" I ask her. "Everyone always says that. Like it's somewhere I should have stayed."

❀ ❀ ❀

Each day, a new letter arrives. I will not open them without
Binky. I wait—several days if I must—so we can read them together. But Diane's calls are part of every night, like washing your
face or taking out your contacts.

"He's not here right now," I say. "Can I take a message?
He's hiking in Canada. He's training for battle. He's taken up
sailing."

❀ ❀ ❀

"Did I tell you?" I say, pouring coffee for two. "We made it into a letter!"

It's a rare morning, to find Binky at the mirror, putting in earrings. The man friend is visiting friends, she explains.

"I'll be late," she says. "But I have my day off tomorrow. We have to talk."

When she's gone, I sit on the edge of my chair and read Diane's letter out loud to the cat.

Michael, I've talked to your lover. She squeaks out lies in her rodent voice. Does she tell you I call? Are you reading this, Rodent? That's your voice on the answering machine!

My heart pounds at this recognition. I'm disappointed some hours later when the voices on the phone are my parents.'

"Come home," says my father. "That Sandy at the high school, she says the kids are clamoring for you. She says they're reworking next year's budget."

My mother says, "Hear this: Joshua Bloom's going through a divorce. He's as handsome as ever."

❅ ❅ ❅

It's Binky's day off; we're coming back from "eating and talking," which turned into not eating and not talking. Things are progressing with the man friend, who takes out the trash and pays rent and knows how to make key lime pie from scratch.

"What does that mean, anyway," I ask her. "What's scratch?"

She hangs behind, pretending she can't hear.

Rounding the corner, I squeak like the rodent I am. Our apartment building, our home, is on fire.

"Look!" I say, gesturing for Binky to hurry up. I grab hold of her arm.

We start to run. The crowd spills off the sidewalk. People are in housedresses with towels on their heads, clutching small dogs, herding children, yelling in Spanish, moving aside in one wave for the fire engines as they come around the corner. One, then two, then three red trucks arrive. The sound itself is an emergency.

What of my yet unpacked boxes? The sweaters will wither in neat folded stacks; the dishes will burst from flaming balls of newspaper. And what of the letters? This is our punishment for keeping them.

"Sugar!" Binky says, and I hate her for saying it first. He's *my* cat, or was; indignation eclipses, for now, fear.

And Binky would leave us both, would rather keep house for the man friend.

I look up then and see people in the building, trapped! They're standing at the windows, calmly. They are in the fire itself, a fire that seems to melt the very windows they press their hands against. Why don't they scream? What do they crane their necks to see?

"It's not our building," Binky says. "Laura, look — a reflection. A trick of the light. Thank God."

The firemen are sending long white ladders up to another building, not ours. The reflection of fire on window glass is like fire behind it. The people in our building are safe, are spectators, too, looking across the street, where the real fire is. I see the actual blaze for a few moments only, before water from the hoses leaves everything in smoke. Around us, people cough and hand out blankets.

"Is anyone hurt? Why no ambulance?" Binky asks.

She addresses our neighbors generally, meeting eyes with no one. There's so much chatter and babble, exclamation and tale-telling, but all of it in Spanish. *I bought that stupid dictionary,* Diane writes, *and we said we'd learn to speak it, but we never did anything but nod and point at things in the bodega. El platano. La patata. La rata.*

"Shh," I say to Binky, listening hard then harder.

"What, now you speak *Español*?" she says.

I know it's ridiculous, like turning down the car radio to find a street address, but how can you not try?

I want to go inside, to cook a pot of noodles, to read today's letter, to finally and really unpack, but we stand there for a few more minutes, just listening.

❖ ❖ ❖

"All this mail and none of it for us," Binky says. "He needs to forward his address. And his stalker."

"We did get the notice for rent," I say.

"Which you can't help with," says Binky, who is looking at me in what feels like the first time in weeks.

In the silence that follows, I eye the light purple envelope in her hand.

"We got a little carried away," she says. "We should change the phone number. And this thing with those people . . ."

"I'll do it," I say. "I'll call first thing tomorrow."

When she leaves to meet her man friend, I rip the sweet-smelling letter open.

❊　❊　❊

"What does it mean?" I ask my father. "You know Spanish, right?"

"He is coming," my father says.

"Who?"

"That's what it means—your billboard. He is coming."

"He as in Jesus?"

"Probably not," says my father. "I mean, I wouldn't count on it."

❊　❊　❊

Sugar sometimes carries a letter, like a kitten, in her mouth.

I dream that Binky carries me just so, then tucks me into bed. She becomes a swan. On her back is Diane, face hidden by hair. She disembarks. She is naked, rising from the bath like a miracle.

In the morning, the sheets and pillow bear an impress. I roll into the shape; I feel a body's heat. Someone was here. Something lingers. A smell, plum and licorice, remains. Here is a curling hair, here a piece of a fingernail, from when it snagged on something in the dark.

When the phone rings, I'm singing and don't want to stop.

"We're happy," I say to Diane.

"I've met someone," I tell my parents.

The letters will stop; one morning the old ones will vanish, too. If Binky comes back, let her stuff them in trash bags. Or let them evaporate, become another state of matter. They'll be the stuff of someone else's sleep. *Él está viniendo!* Here are the long white feathers I pulled from the pillow. These are evidence, an incarnation of you.

❊　❊　❊

When I go downstairs to check the mail, Diane is there. She sits on the steps, knees in her arms, wearing a striped dress and boots. I say her name. She is herself and no one else.

"I came by to see if he'd talk to me. I've seen you," she says, shy for a moment. "But I never see him. I wasn't sure if you were you—or if that other woman that comes by, if she was you. Your sister? I gave her a light in the park once."

I stand on the step above her, looking down, fiddling with the keys. She touches my leg.

"I'm Laura," I say.

"Is he home?"

"No. Maybe. Do you want to come up?"

I hear our heartbeats echo in the stairwell. Or maybe it's just our feet. We walk inside and she looks around, runs her hand along the shelf under the mirror, looks at the bare walls, the boxes, the curtain-less windows. As if to see something hidden, she stands on the tips of her toes.

"Would you stay for dinner?" I ask. "We have pasta, the bowties."

She sits in the only chair. The letters are scattered around her like petals. *He loves me. He loves me not.*

"It must get to you," she chokes out. "He doesn't even try to hide them!"

I go into the kitchen, put water on the stove. I stand in the doorway and look at her.

She sits in what's left of the natural light, in a cloud of illuminated dust mites. The pigeons have gone silent. Diane reads her own letters, touching her fingers to the words. When she leans forward, I can't see her face.

"He's coming home, any minute now."

I kneel beside her and pick up a letter. She smells like the apartment, as if she were the wallpaper peeled from it.

"I'll wait," Diane says. "Thank you."

She slips off her boots and one panty-hosed toe skims my calf. The touch is so real I can hear it: the slither of nylon on skin. On the sill, pigeons bleat.

So we wait—for water to boil, for love to come and carry us away.

Slow Flies

In Tanzania, above the beaded
collars of the Maasai, flies
crawl on smooth brown faces,
settle in eyes that stare as I stare back.
Our guide says the flies cause trachoma.
Millions have gone blind.
The flies pick up *Chlamydia trachomatis*
while feeding and laying eggs
on dung and feces. Repeated infections
scar people's eyelids, turning
the lashes inward. Every time they blink,
their lashes scrape their eyeballs.
Seeking relief,
they pull out their lashes with tweezers.
Now, in a cottage in Maine,
I'm having tea with friends. Flies buzz
inside the windows, despite the open
window through which they could easily
pass, choosing instead to endlessly
walk on glass. They lift off, land,
start over, ignoring our blackberry tarts,
the dish of honey for tea,
whereas we consume
the tarts, and tea with honey,
eagerly, talking all the while of poetry,
and Marilyn recites a villanelle
by Elizabeth Bishop in which the word
disaster occurs repeatedly.

Kata Juta

The law Wally said must be followed
if you break the law then you will be hunted
punished this is the way
a friend yelled don't go into the hills
it is not meant for you to go
I went to see Kata Juta the Olgas anyway
and climbed the burly glued-together mounds of rocks
but no spears caught my upper leg
I continued to climb listening to the red stone and sky
feeling safe in the groves of desert spruce
where the arched-necked goanna angled through the bush
and the yellow wist wist bird flew down
for it had rained the other day and small pools
of fresh water sat waiting for them both on the rock

Juan Franco, photograph

From *Trying to Remember*

Add-a-Pearl Necklace

It was the family joke that he —
ever the accountant —
wed at the year's end to claim dependents
while I was born costing money.

A New Year's baby, my arrival was a sore spot
when his wife witnessed my homecoming
instead of coming home.
Their thirty-seventh anniversary
came the day before my birth — fitting,
I've thought, since their love led to me.

Every year it was the same.
For my birthday she would give me a pearl
and a teddy bear calendar
with the note *On your happy day.*
The necklace would be restrung
and I would count my new age with my teeth,
sliding each pearl like a chorus line
across my gentle bite.

When her handwriting wasn't hers on my eighth,
I didn't notice. When my ninth turned
from Teddy to tulips I dismissed Mom's cursive
and bit down on my gritty pearl.
We never spoke of the absent bears
or altered scrawl. She would surrender the gift each year
This is from Grandma
and another pearl would be added.

Radio Free Me

In algebra I learned that what's called the *given* isn't open to question, and Henry James informed me that the *donnée* of a novel can't be criticized. What's been given to me includes my parents and consequently their decisions, their relationship, their genes. To analyze what was going on with them, to try mastering this newly complicated trigonometry, felt unnatural. For a neat freak like me this unexpected apocalypse of disorderliness was hard to bear. As I saw it, whatever drama my parents' lives had ought to have ended the second I was born. At the dénouement of a conventional love story they'd picked each other, then made me, their only child. That should have been the end, as regards them. Dad liked being a bank officer; Mom worked off and on as an educational consultant and appeared content with or without a contract. I was their *numero uno.* It was only natural that they should stand over me solid and sheltering, like a triumphal arch. Now it felt like the arch of resentment. My parents simply weren't supposed to have emotional lives, certainly not operatic ones that dwarfed my own.

Our white Dutch colonial stood stoutly in an affable suburb, which wasn't too raw, thanks to its big old maples, beeches, and oaks. Everything was nice there — teachers, friends, parks, shops. The disaffected kept out of sight, stayed in their basements, went Goth, lived on their computers. As I grew up my parents encouraged each of my ephemeral enthusiasms: rocks, salamanders, gymnastics, ballet, mythology, Emily Dickinson, musical theater, tennis, the radio. They delighted in my minuscule achievements, helped with my papers, reviewed my college applications, listened to my fake broadcasts. They charmed my friends and I can't with justice accuse them of being either too permissive or too strict. In return, I never rebelled, never went through the awful stage of negative self-definition that I both admired and feared in Whitney. When I was a freshman I was drawn to Whitney's sophisticated, self-destructive personality as to an anti-self. I was impressed by her inability to live smoothly, yet as a sophomore I didn't want to cohabit with it. Witnessing her chaos was like going to the movies. I was well adjusted, happy to have no siblings and pitied those who did. Sure, marriages had been detonating around me for years but it never occurred to me that divorce could blow up my own triad, that our stability could ever be precarious, inconceivable that either of my parents could care enough about anybody else to unbalance our three-legged stool. Now that it was happening my mother had adopted an attitude of resignation. Her passivity incensed *her* mother, my Nana, who wanted my father's head on her well-and-tree. Mom just didn't have any fight in her; it was as if she agreed that, next to the tragic younger woman, this exotic Jelena, she was nothing but a cartoon of American womanhood, just another weight-obsessed middle-class consumer of televised opinions and consumer frippery. As for Dad, well, he even *looked* like a pillar of society, a gray-templed, tie-wearing emblem of rectitude. These given parents represented the world and now it appeared the world wasn't what I thoughtlessly took it to be. Turns out the world isn't stable, more Greek temple than Roman arch. Reality is supposed to be predictable, not some breathtaking spectacle. Now I had discovered that stability is always precarious, that even aqueducts collapse. Safe at college, I couldn't shake the feeling of having absconded from a burning town. Sure, looking back at conflagrations can turn you into a pillar of salt. But who can help looking?

❖ ❖ ❖

Nana began to phone three, four times every week, claiming to be anxious about me.

"How are you doing, Pumpkin?" Not *how are you* but how are you *doing, Pumpkin*. That is: you're still an infant, plump with baby fat and helpless.

"I'm okay, Nana. Really."

Nana brushed aside my assurances the way a ghost-hunter would cobwebs, eager to come to grips with the spirits. What she yearned for was to count the ways in which her resourceless Pumpkin *wasn't* okay and the still more numerous ways in which she herself was aggrieved and how little she merited her worrying. Maybe she even hoped to find out that her problem-grandchild was finally dating an appropriate boy. In short, this was a case of grandmotherly wound-probing.

Nana has always been an exacting inquisitor. Do you have many friends? Are you going to make valedictorian? Which colleges have you heard from? Do you *really* think you should be eating things like that, dear? She likes poking her finger where it hurts: can you feel this? or this? Here, here?

"Have you spoken to her since yesterday? She tells me exactly nothing, you know, her own mother." Nana's voice crumbles dramatically, like her pound cake. "I just cry myself to sleep every night." Implication: don't *you* cry *yourself* to sleep too . . . Pumpkin?

"I talk to her *every* day, Nana."

"And?"

"What can I tell you? She's holding up."

Nana's indignation put the starch back in her voice. "What does that mean, *holding up*? What is she—a dam?"

My dam is a dam, holding back a million gallons of tears, and I'm the little cowering town that stands to get flooded if she ever cracks. Metaphors are every bit as false as they are true.

"Nana, what's she supposed to do?"

"*Do?* I have a few ideas," she growled menacingly. "To start with she could hire one of those barracuda divorce lawyers."

I let this pass. I counted to three. "I got an A- on my Russian history paper." I didn't know what else to say. "It was on the Civil War," I added desperately.

There was a brief silence and then Nana said, "Minus?"

❖ ❖ ❖

Whitney's my best friend. She and I were going to room together this year but at the last minute I lost my nerve and stuck with my single. I was prudent, which is to say selfish. To live with Whitney would have meant having three phantom roommates: Whitney's eating disorder, her mood swings, and her shrink. And, much as I loved her, I couldn't face living with all of these. I'm the sort of person who'll haul her humongous superego all the way around the block to avoid guilt, which well-read Whitney calls "the old agenbite of inwit." Being my best friend, she accepted my decision after I'd explained it for about three hours.

Whitney's one of those people who are wise about everybody except themselves. Maybe it's a sort of wound-and-bow thing; her psychological insight about herself is absolute zero yet it's infallible for others, often cruelly so. "You can't argue people into loving you, or *not* loving you," she observed over one of our dinners. She was expatiating on my parents, with my tacit permission. I'd called a pow-wow, thrown my cap on our usual table at the back of the dining hall, and told her pretty much everything I knew about what was going on.

"Look, compassion can be as irresistible as lust—more in fact, since it's such a popular virtue. The way I see it, your father believes he's acting generously, that his *soul's* gotten bigger. Ever try to argue somebody out of doing something they think is really, *really* good?"

"But *is* it good?"

"No, I think it sucks, but I took ethics last semester so how should I know? I'd say the point is *he* thinks it's good. That's not only gratifying but also convenient. What do *you* think?"

"I think I'm pretty useless, no good to either of them. My grandmother seems to think I should be cracking up and getting a 4.0."

Whitney smirked. She's not incapable of sympathy but, like so many fascinating and exasperating people, she defines herself by her problems and it seems to her natural that others should do the same. She's smart in a funny, self-lacerating way, and over six feet tall. Once, lamenting the dearth of basketball players attracted to bulimics their own size, she sighed, "Just another problem I'll never outgrow." Whitney considers happiness suspect. Happy people make good roommates but don't teach you much. If Whitney were a chair, she'd have no upholstery. Even as it is, she has hardly any padding, morally as well as physically.

"Want to hear how they met?"

"Sure." She stopped not eating to look at me attentively.

"It had something to do with *me*, at least indirectly. My clothes, that is. Back in September my parents called and told me this woman's horror story. Jelena's, I mean. Mom said she'd asked the Pevics, who were taking her in, if she could help and found out that Jelena was about my size, so would it be all right to give her some of the things I'd left in my closet—you know, high-school stuff? It made me feel kind of funny. I mean I didn't care about the clothes, but I felt sad about this totally destitute refugee getting them because even if she didn't like them she wouldn't be able to turn them down without seeming ungrateful. I mean here's this grown woman who's been through all kinds of shit and she's offered hand-me-downs like a poor cousin or a little sister, *my* little sister. I pictured her in my high-school outfits. It made a weird sort of bond, I guess, but what I thought at the time was that it was just insulting. I wanted to say that if they insisted on giving this Jelena something to wear they should just buy *new* stuff but that would have sounded mean, like I *begrudged* her the clothes. You know?"

Whitney heaved one of her best dramatic sighs.

"What is it?" I asked impatiently.

She played with a spoonful of pudding. "Nothing," she said. "Come *on*."

"Well, I was just thinking about how it might make *me* feel—I mean, *my* clothes, *my* father, *my* mom's husband. I think I'd feel as if I were being, I don't know, *tossed overboard*. You're an only child and your mom's an only wife. Or at least she used to be."

As I said, Whitney could be cruel, though she took no pleasure in it, which is to her credit. I remember thinking that someday I should get Whitney and Nana together. It would be like introducing a humidifier to a de-humidifier. I could lock them in the same room for an hour and see which one came out.

※　※　※

Facts never reveal as much as people think. Knowing the facts just gives you the illusion of knowing, even if, like me, you're not away at college majoring in communications, writing papers on how the Red Army beat the White Army, or memorizing the Ten Principles of Good Journalism, which was a topic of complaint at another dinner confab. "It's all just stupid regurgitating," said Whitney about my newswriting class with Professor Swanson. She liked to be supercilious about my major. It amused her to call this particular course, required of all communications concentrators, *Introduction to the Fundamentals of Basics*.

I was irritated and defensive. "Nobody ever says that about drivers' tests. Anyway, you should be an expert on regurgitation. Nothing ever comes up the same as it went down, does it?"

※　※　※

Here's how I picture it.

Jelena finds it hard to move but she makes her way down the sidewalk, crosses the street, trudges up to the green door. Jelena's no Stoic but she's *stoical*; that is, she can tyrannize over herself but only so much. She is a woman condemned to feel everything. Anybody who took the trouble to look closely at her would be bound to see everything that's roiling under her frozen foreign face. The doorbell seems to her too impersonal, not direct enough, and so with an effort she commits herself to knocking. She strikes the door tentatively, as if expecting the wood to burn her knuckles. She's seen that the car is in the driveway but this isn't to say she's thinking clearly, even though thinking is what people do when everything else fails and everything else has certainly failed Jelena.

Mother comes to the door wearing a sweatsuit because she doesn't feel up to putting on anything more hopeful. I like to imagine she'd know who it was without standing on tiptoe to peep out the narrow windows at the top of the door.

What do they say—either of them? Who speaks first?

Jelena's rigid face dissolves. She's not greedy and anything but triumphant. In fact, she's beside herself. In a gesture from another world she opens her hands, palms up. What am I to do? She beats her chest and head like somebody who really knows how to beat herself, like a woman who, when it comes to anguish, is a virtuoso. Jelena *wails*, just not out loud. Her English is not good but it's good enough.

I imagine her saying, "If I killed myself would that do good?" Would that do good.

❖ ❖ ❖

Silence is golden only because it's so malleable. I hadn't had a word of explanation or expiation from my father—nada, zilch— just a note on bank stationery telling me what number to call if there were an emergency. Nothing at the end but "Dad," no *yours most sincerely*, let alone *love*. What was I supposed to make of that? Either he didn't love me anymore or didn't feel he had the right to tell me he did, which was nearly as bad. You can rely on me, shouted the subtext, *but only if it's a matter of life and death*.

I'm romantic enough to grant that love must be served. I'm also cynical enough to see this Jelena business as his mid-life crisis. Maybe I'm even deep enough to see what my father's doing as serious, *fatal* even. I was prepared to rise to the occasion; I just needed to know which occasion it was. Shouldn't he have been trying to reassure me? On the phone one night Mother said forlornly, "Who can compete with all that pain? It's so—vivid." She meant that she felt pale beside Jelena; and, to tell the truth, I was feeling a bit shadowy myself. I'd never even laid eyes on this woman and Mom didn't describe her. I was free to picture her as a sexpot. But maybe she's ugly, or just a wisp of feminine pain around a pair of huge Balkan eyes. All I knew for sure was that she was a size six. I only guessed she was willing to kill herself, to ask—"would that do good?" I even tried taking her side. I imagined my father pestering her, his badgering being directly proportional to how much she unintentionally pestered *him*. She was all the suffering in the world. Does loving pain make a man feel saintly and so willing to sacrifice everything and everybody to the idol of his own saintliness? Was this my father's shot at leper-licking? Is tragedy *that* enchanting?

Facts, then. Once upon a time Jelena was a young wife and new mother. She lived with her husband and infant son someplace in the Balkans. The Balkans can be very pretty with all their forests and rivers. The photographs I've seen all show the nature without the history. Under the picturesque mountains the ravines are full of corpses, several strata of them.

So there was a vicious war. Jelena's husband and son were both killed and she was raped. Somehow she wound up in Germany and Mr. Pevic, who's related to her in some baroque fashion, an uncle's second cousin or something, sponsored her immigration. This is how Jelena came to be in our tidy American suburb, penniless, traumatized, helpless, clothesless, bereft, and evidently irresistible to middle-aged bankers.

According to the Ten Rules of Good Journalism, knowing all this I ought to know something, but it seems there's a big difference between news and a news story.

Was it clandestine? Trysts in motels? Tawdry lies about working late? Did Jelena resist him or respond, try to fight off his insistence or give in at once? And did he struggle against it or jump in with both feet? Did new love make him poetic? Were the Pevics aware of what was afoot? Did they abet it, eager to get the woman off their hands? Was it, like a lot of affairs, sordid from the outside but noble from within? Was she just interested in his money? Was Dad impelled by simple infatuation or by an inexorable longing to protect? Did the answer lie in the allure of reality after years of bland illusion? Is love the highest or the lowest? Is a guillotine heavy or light?

I'm unaccustomed to passion, never having seen that much of it. I'm a suburban girl—nice, like the houses and the cars and the schools—but all the while there was this asteroid out there headed my way. I felt as though my undramatic life had imploded, or at least somebody's had.

❊   ❊   ❊

From the age of ten my secret ambition was to be on the radio. This was why I chose to major in communications. Radio is safer than television, poorer but purer, less popular but more intimate. "Find your own voice," Professor Swanson exhorted us on the first day. In her mouth the phrase rang like a battle cry, a shibboleth, a dogma. But there was something desperate about her enthusiasm. What about grammar and spelling, I wondered, should they also be creative, individuated? Find your *own* voice? It was her way of telling us that, so far as she was concerned, the class was a legal fiction, that we were all distinct and should admire her because she would cherish all our voices, one at a time.

Well, I already had a voice, such as it was. I wanted to use it, too. In fact, my wish was to be a bodiless voice, an invisible consolation to an invisible listener, distanced and familiar at once.

In September I used my own voice to talk my way into an internship at the university's student-run radio station. There was no question of my getting my own show, of course. The place is big on what they call *paying dues*, which means at least two semesters of scut-work and ass-kissing. I worked for a guy named Billy Bristoe, a senior who did have his own show. Billy was a bit of a jerk, an untalented wise-ass who thought himself hilarious. He played alternative rock and did these mock-interviews with his pals. It almost goes without saying that Billy was a sexist pig, but he was smart enough never to say anything too offensive on air himself. He let his friends say the outrageous things and set himself up as the cool, laid-back purveyor of rusty ironies.

"So I was telling her like how hot my French instructor is, you know. I mean a chick speaking French at nine in the morning can be a real turn-on. And then she goes all huffy and says how I was objectifying Dr. Varenne. Crap like that. She's majoring in Women's Studies. Big surprise."

"I'm minoring in that," Billy says dryly.

Bristoe's Show, as he called it, was on from nine to eleven three nights a week. I set up the tapes; I fetched the Starbucks, wrote out the announcements and told the guests who showed up too drunk or stoned to go home. Whitney took to calling me the Cinderella of the Sound Check. I was paying my dues.

Late one Tuesday afternoon I got a call from Charlie Zuckerman, Billy's roommate. They'd been playing hall hockey and the long and the short of it was that Billy was in the infirmary.

"Could you cover for him? I mean, could you do the show?"

"Do the *show*?"

"Yeah. I already tried Savitt but he isn't picking up and that Weiser dude claims he has to write some paper. Look, Billy says all you have to do is play stuff for a couple of hours. You can pick the disks, he doesn't care."

"How *is* good old Bill?"

"Oh, he's okay. Just broke something."

"Too bad. Nothing *essential*, I hope, nothing *life*-threatening?"

"Nope."

"Fine. Tell him not to worry."

"You'll do it, then?"

I sat on my excitement. "Sure. Why not?"

❖ ❖ ❖

I decided to adopt the Bristoe formula, music interrupted by an interview. I called Whitney. In a panicky voice she said microphones made her phobic. So I guilt-tripped her. I reminded her my father was leaving my mother for an immigrant and that I didn't need any more stress. "Besides," I said, "*everything* makes you phobic."

"I'm a philosophy major," she reminded me, "and consider broadcasting beneath my dignity."

"But you don't have any dignity," I pointed out sweetly.

Whitney grumbled. "If philosophy isn't good for dignity, what's left?"

I was encouraging. "Okay, you're afraid of being on the air. I hear you. So just pretend to be somebody else, somebody who *isn't* scared of microphones. And remember, I haven't even *heard* from my father. My Nana calls almost every night to turn the knife. And my *mother's* cataleptic."

"All right, all right. I'll do it. But under protest."

"Noted."

After dinner we headed to the studio. It was raining and we had only one umbrella. We giggled as we bunched under it, as though we were in a French movie.

Whitney had never been inside the Com building before. The place seemed to make her more anxious. Uncharacteristically, she gave herself up to my authority.

"Who should I pretend to be?"

"Ludwig Wittgenstein's great-niece. Who cares? Anybody you like."

She brightened a little. "Can I pretend to be a shock jock?"

"Sure."

"How about a right-wing bloviast?"

"Knock yourself out," I laughed.

Whitney looked around at the lobby's grimy walls and its cascading bulletin boards.

"Christ. This place looks like my high school," she said.

"Except for the hall passes and metal detectors you'd hardly know the difference," I quipped, shaking out the umbrella.

We took the elevator, the studio being on the top floor, and waited outside the glass partition for Sean Amoroso to finish his sports show. Whitney whispered in my ear. "He looks kind of tall. How tall *is* he?"

"Yeah, he *is* tall, I guess."

I took a stack of CDs out of my bag. All girls, from Baez to Bangles to Benatar.

The sight of tall Sean surrounded by all that equipment seemed to put Whitney into a kind of caffeine fit. She was fidgeting mightily.

"Are you having a mood swing or do you just have to pee?" I asked.

"Can we make *calls*?" she asked. "I mean can we call people up and talk to them on the *air*? Is that *legal*?"

"Well, there's a phone," I said uncertainly, looking up into two preternaturally brilliant blue eyes.

* * *

We took over the studio at nine o'clock sharp. Like a biblio-
phile in her first bookstore, Whitney walked around scrutinizing
the equipment. "What's *this* do?" she asked.

"Shh," I hissed.

I signed on, clumsily explaining that Billy B. was indisposed
owing to a hockey mishap, assuring whatever audience he had that
it was nothing critical. "So I'll be sitting in. We're going to have
a sort of Sadie Hawkins night," I said and showed Whitney how
to play the first track we'd decided on, Janis Joplin's *Piece of My
Heart*. "You've got to start hot," I had insisted as we grabbed our
CDs.

The minute Joplin began wailing my nerves settled down. I
leaned back and considered my friend. We were wearing the same
brand of jeans. Our hair was cut in the same fashion, to the same
length. We strove to be indistinguishable yet were certain of our
distinction. We wanted this year's look, this season's labels, but
believed we wore them with a difference. Post-adolescent conformity weighs a lot; it takes effort to look like everybody else. Perhaps beauty itself is a species of conformity. I thought of outland-
ish Jelena in my dated jumpers and pastel tops, an emblem of the
irreparable sorrows of the Old World in a calico sundress. Did he
love dressing her, dressing her like me, *un*dressing her? Was *that*
it? It must be painful to fall in love with pain. If she were ugly,
was her ugliness a relief?

After the Joplin, Whitney and I began a desultory conversation about the sociological significance of coed dorms, the pros
and cons of sexual demystification, followed by gender equality in
sports, which was something of an obsession with Whitney, though
nobody could be less athletic.

"Two generations ago girls would play indoors in twos or
threes," she said. "They favored preserving relationships over
winning and ended a game as soon as there was a dispute. Now
it's the soccer league, the basketball team; it's crew and lacrosse. I
mean we're being raised the same as boys, athletically speaking.
It's bound to affect our moral development. It's going to make us
go to law school and support wars."

"Wars? Aren't you exaggerating a bit?" I asked in the style
of Barbara Walters.

"Nah, I don't think so. Guys are all legalists, even the worst of them. They love *rules*. Ever notice that when they watch football what excites them the most isn't the touchdown but the disputed call? Was his foot in or out? Fifty replays from different angles. My last boyfriend used to say the greatest invention of the twentieth century was instant replay."

"So you're saying boys like disputes and so they become lawyers and warmongers?"

"Sort of. Like I said, they're legalistic. They judge by principles, not personalities. They'll step on their best friend's *face* to get into the end-zone and the best friend won't even mind. They like the death penalty, most of them. An eye for an eye. Case closed. Facts and the law, period. Girls used to be humane relativists, used to have to know all the details, the whole story with all the extenuations. To understand is to forgive. Now not so much. Foot in or foot out. Winning trumps friendship."

"More music," I said, making a gun of my fingers, and pointing it at Whitney. Her train of thought derailed, she pouted. "It's girls' night in—or on," I said breezily. "How about a little red-dirt from Emmy Lou Harris?"

Whitney resentfully pushed the buttons. "Game before friends," I said with a shrug. Whitney got to her feet. She was jangling from shoulder to foot like one of those hinged Halloween skeletons. She squatted down and rooted in my bag, pulled out my telephone book and waved it at me with a wicked grin.

"Okay. So how do I get on the phone?" she said.

✿ ✿ ✿

Caesar ignored the prophecy; Napoleon invaded Russia; Western Union laughed at Alex Bell; Gide flipped Proust a rejection slip; and Decca sent the Beatles packing. The worst mistakes are always the ones you can't remember making. When you look back at your follies it's not your specious reasoning or miscalculations that really get you but the goofs you can't imagine having made for any reason at all.

Say I was busy, distracted. Say it was my first time on air. Say Whitney mesmerized me with her neurotic flair. Say that at the wrong moment I fell into some *je m'en fiche* wormhole. Who knows? In any case, I let Whitney hook the phone up on air, let her seize control, didn't stop her when she opened my phone book, didn't say *I'll bet it's my father how could you stop right now what are you thinking?* Nope, I let go, didn't act responsibly. Looking back, I suppose the sheer relief of *laissez-tomber* played a big part in the renunciation of my radio captaincy. I let myself believe it actually pleased me to hand things over to my friend, to wash my hands, to satisfy my curiosity while still being technically innocent, to sit back and listen for the smash of pediment on plinth.

❊ ❊ ❊

My father's new number had become like an alarm behind glass, a reluctant invitation: *Break in Case of Emergency.* Of course I didn't know for sure that Whitney meant to call him; nevertheless, I guessed the moment she began pushing buttons. I felt a little passage of nausea. Suddenly the studio stank, reeked of body odor under a thin curtain of ozone, like Frankenstein's lab. The fluorescent lights bore down on us purply, washing out every softening shadow. All the edges looked sharp and Whitney, jumping from one foot to the other, struck me as unhealthier than ever, alarmingly jazzed.

Why did he have to be there? I didn't even know where *there* was, or if that pathetic woman was with him. But Whitney punched in the numbers; she was confident and ready. She smiled at me, fumbled and even found the switch for the speaker so we could both hear whatever was going to go pulsing out into the world. I might still have stopped her. I could have.

Nothing daunted Whitney's reckless freedom, which, like Joplin's, was another name for nothing left to lose. Freshman year she'd disappeared for two days. I was anxious all weekend then appalled—but also impressed—when she came back and said she'd been skydiving, stepping out of airplanes.

From the first her tone was offensive. "That you, Mr. Bank President?"

"Hello? Who's this?" He sounded a little terrified, the way he always did when the phone rang after nine o'clock at night. It was my father's voice but for the first time I heard it as the voice of a man.

"Hello. Glad to have caught you in. So, sir, what would you like to say to your daughter?"

I looked at Whitney; Whitney looked at the ceiling.

"My daughter? Is she *there*?"

"Maybe. But we'd rather you talked to *me*, as you've shown no inclination to give her a buzz lately. Not that we don't respect your privacy and all but we'd really prefer you talked to me. I'm her friend. Her *good* friend. Her best, I'd say."

"Which one are you?"

"Which *one*? Does it matter? Okay, I'm Rachel Wittgenstein. Perhaps she mentioned me?"

"Not that I remember."

"*Hélas. Quel dommage.* Anyway, what would you say to your daughter if she *were* listening? Hypothetically."

There was a long pause, a noise like someone rattling change in a pocket, then my father's voice resumed, sounding a little strangled. "I'd say I'm sorry." There was just the tiniest caesura between *I'm* and *sorry*.

"Sorry? That's *it*? You're *sorry*? Well, okay. But, tell me, what *for*, exactly? I'd honestly like to know."

"Look. What is it—Rachel? Rachel, this isn't fair . . . I'm not an eloquent man, not prepared—"

"Not *eloquent*? Now I call that an odd thing to say. I mean I asked you a simple question and I've got a few more, ones your daughter would probably like answered. You know, hypothetically. I don't see the need for *eloquence*. Just the contrary, in fact."

"I'm sorry if I hurt her. I know it must—"

"*If*? Well, excuse *me* for jumping to conclusions. So, does she love you?"

"My daughter?"

"Jelena, *obviously*. The victim of history. The pietà of Belgrade. Does she love you?"

Another pause. Bed springs. No click.

"I don't know. Maybe. Sometimes she makes me think so. But then she says she *can't*."

I couldn't believe it; my buttoned-up sire was opening his heart. And to Whitney of all people. I didn't want to hear a word, or to miss one.

Whitney pounced. "Can't love *you*?"

"Anybody."

"I see. But you love *her*. I mean we can at least establish that, right?"

"Too much, I guess. Look, things happen. Nobody could be more surprised than I am."

"Yes, I can see how it must have come as quite a shock to you. And your wife, your daughter? Is it that you don't love them; that is, not *enough*?"

"No, no. I love them *too*. Look—"

I really wanted to intervene. Truly, I yearned to stop it. I even groped towards Whitney but she pulled away. Something was happening in her. She was moving jerkily and looked manic.

"Look nothing," she snapped. "It's a shitty way to treat them. But of course you know that. You know you're being a shit but still you go right on being one. In fact, you're such an *absolute* shit you think being a shit isn't being a shit *at all*. Am I right?"

"Look here, I don't have to—"

"Oh yes, you *do*. You *do* need to listen to this. Betrayals always cry out for revenge, don't they? So maybe it's already begun for you. Maybe I'm the avenging angel. Me, little Rachel Wittgenstein. Have you considered that you've just made this miserable Jelena even more miserable? Do you really suppose she could be happy at somebody else's expense . . . *after what she's been through*? I mean, *do* you?"

My father, in extremis now, mumbled, "She needs me. Needs me more."

"More than your *daughter*? More than your *wife*? So what *is* she to you, exactly? A *new* daughter or a new *wife* or both wrapped up in one fetching imported package? Saint Pauli Girl. That's pretty sick, you ask me. Selfish and *sick*, wouldn't you say?"

Whitney was now thrashing around the cramped studio, all twisted up in wires. Stories I didn't know were colliding, sliding into and over one another like eels in a bucket, like tectonic plates.

"Tell me something *else*, then." She was shrieking now. I could see the spittle flying from her mouth, green under the fluorescent lights. "Did you ever want to *rape* your daughter? Did you maybe even *do* it?"

❖ ❖ ❖

Through my lone window I've been watching the first snow of the year float down. The gigantic wet flakes make it look like an airborne assault on the campus by a Lilliputian army. It's the sort of snow that soundproofs the world. I turned out the light to see it better.

Dormitory cells fall between the provisional permanence of a teenager's bedroom and the frank transience of a motel cube. Whatever character they have is plastered on, a matter of comforters, hair dryers, posters, all chosen at the same time, all meant to be tossed aside the moment real life begins. No wonder they call the grand finale of this four-year distention of adolescence commencement.

Where do I go for Christmas? And how do I behave when I get there? Resigned like mother, bereft like Jelena; should I be turbulent, volatile, serene? Please, Professor Swanson, what are the Ten Rules I'm supposed to follow?

According to my collegiate dictionary the word *sacrifice* means to make holy. But it doesn't say what's made holy, the thing that's renounced or the person who does the renouncing. Betrayal might just be a failed sacrifice, sacrifice merely a successfully rationalized betrayal. It all depends on your perspective. Didn't Whitney say that once upon a time we girls were reared to be yielding relativists, forgiving Madonnas who will listen to the whole story and eschew judgment? It all depends. An old joke of my father's: Why do firemen wear red suspenders? *It all depends on you.*

Somehow news of my broadcast got to Mother. If Dad told her, I wonder how he described it. I could tell she would have liked to be furious with me but what hurt the most was how she couldn't quite manage it, the fury, I mean. She was in total lockdown. But then she told Nana and Nana wanted to know *exactly* what was said. She demanded a transcript. Not surprisingly, my father, who finally hung up on Whitney, has gone on not calling. I tried phoning him but he's changed his magic number. There's no reaching him now, even in an emergency. Thus did I learn that even radio isn't what you could call safe.

❊ ❊ ❊

Somehow I got Whitney back to her room and into bed. As I tucked her in, a gangling, burbling infant, I recalled the way she used to oversleep her freshman year, how often I'd tried to get her up for early classes. "Why the hell do you sleep so much?" I'd asked with what must have struck her as stunning innocence.

Whitney had replied airily, like a world-weary grande dame, "Practicing, my dear, practicing."

She cut her wrists, probably somewhere around dawn. Luckily, she did it in the communal bathroom and the girl who found her didn't panic. Unlike Billy Bristoe, what put Whitney in the infirmary *was* life-threatening. They kept her there for five days then sent her home, covering her nakedness with that decorous academic euphemism, *medical withdrawal.*

I sympathize with my mother's emptiness and hope it may gradually be filled again. Who knows? Unhappiness might do wonders for her. Already her friends have closed protectively around her and, no doubt, are drawing up lists of divorcés and widowers. Sometimes I think I can almost understand how my father, after decades of juiceless routine, pointless work, vapid vacations, stupid movies, Rotary luncheons, building funds, charity drives, PTA meetings, saw that misery and loss are real and fell for them. After all, it was Jelena's distilled, all-but-irremediable need he blamed, not his own. All he wanted was to dress it up in my abandoned, out-of-date normality, my stupid outgrown happiness.

Corry Parker, photograph

Monday, My Love

To say of the heart that it eats rice for
breakfast, scuffs its nails, puts in the
recycle bin so many old letters. And

it is Monday already, and the heart
is gone to war. Those other organs also,
the eye for instance, devouring everything

and spouting out little tears. The
kidney, with its predisposition
towards frequency: come collect

me in your little jars. Oh spleen.
Oh spleen. The intestine held
onto me so dearly while I wept.

Don't, he said, and wrapped his
thin arms round. My love, it is
Monday already and the house

of my body is so strong and so
good.

Love Song

Come, love, be biddable. Do.
Woo again, as once you did,
without this heavy load of sighs.
Rest your restlessness, dear,
between my thighs. Be languid now
upon the bolster. It means you no harm.
Content you in content again. Love,
leave off that thought of hunt or sport.
Leave it there upon the lintel.
Her buttermilk shoulder,
her slender ankle will keep, love.
My gaze has never wavered.

Won't you come, love? Be biddable, pray.
This day, this night in our sateen tent
content you once again with me.

Fremont

To my old dog and faithful friend, inspired by Song #15
"Here I Love You," Pablo Neruda's Twenty Love Poems
and a Song of Despair

Here I love you
The night sings
And the horizon hides in vain

In the dark
The wind disentangles itself from the moon
A TV glow on vagrant waters
Dancing figures chase a processional of leaving
And you so suddenly gone
Are like the high stars
Hidden by the clouds of night

Sometimes I get up early
In a hot sweat
Far away from sea sounds
There is no port
And the horizon hides you

Here I love you
Among these cold things
My long strokes cannot wake you

They founder
Like a tanker in a Great Lakes storm
Crossing an inland sea
With no arrival

Not really a person
I see you forgotten
Like old anchors at some park monument

Here I wonder
Are the piers lonely
When the afternoon does not moor there?

Stretched out as if asleep on the hallway carpet
Memory wrestles with the slow twilight
Of what should have been
The night comes
And I can no longer hear it sing.

From the collection of the Editor

The River

> . . . On all sides I hear
> the vanishing of isolated larks.
> — *W. H. Auden*

I've come back to the ancient river I left long ago
— narrow channel of conformity then — its current
gnawing at slick black banks where it passed
through Hog Walker's farm. . . where I was baptized

while the congregation sang, "Take Me to the River
to Pray" from a riverbank sandbar. . . where I would
later build "hideouts" from things deposited by
the flooding river. . . where a drowned deer once

caught in a branch of a tree taken by the flood, a
torn red blanket covering its strangling until coyotes
dragged it down night by night, bone by bone — white
bloated necks of Leopard Frogs singing Requiem.

From Phoenix fires I built of driftwood, sunflower stalks
and white bones of birds and animals killed by flood
and time, wispy white smoke rising slowly into diamond
stars and blue black nights. . . fine gray ash giving its

life back to the river in rain and spring melt. From
this womb I watched squadrons of birds fly south
to climes I tried to imagine while I listened to cleft
hooves of Lute Walls' cows suck their way through

mud-silk ooze of artesian swamps, and blue herons
work the River in their bluish whiteness, hard yellow
eyes splitting the water for fish I could not see.
World I thought existed because I was there.

※

Old Dutch Elms—slashed open by time and lightning—
stand half in and half out of the river, exposed
roots coiling back toward pitch black earth cut away
by flood and smooth-browed time. I ride the river's

memory now, searching for harbors against the
dreamy desolation of places I could know only with
my mind. Each whirlpool riding the current circles
inside of me. . . each bubble rising to the surface

becomes the air I breathe. . . each glint of river silt holds
me to shared secrets and the repair of wounded
arteries walking in this new silver ribbon of moonlight
in Haddan's pasture. . . where buffalo once wallowed,

and the Oregon Trail passed. . . where Eden slapped
itself alive against mudslick gumbo and blood pulse
of a boy floating on his back, taut-skinned belly staring
down the sky, while his mother's off-key voice took

wild flight above him in ponderous Lutheran hymns,
her wicked delight in spontaneous sentences attacking
the Devil's temptations at Wednesday Night Prayer
Meetings—counterpoint to whispering cottonwoods.

✳

On Indian summer afternoons, a neighbor's old dog
coaxes me down to the river to throw sticks, his thick
body doing its comic parody of a once lithe lightness.
When he tires he lies down beside me on a pink sliver

of sand, and we watch the glory of water gliders make
their long-legged speed runs on backwater puddles,
stilling the eye in their race against late afternoon light.

✳

Leaving the river before I knew the difference between
necessity and innocence, I've carried the river with me

into a world where no mysteries—no true mysteries—
ever get solved, its riverstones a kind of blessing on

life's incompleteness, stones changing the river as the
river changes the stones, what ancients called "knowing
the mind of god." Rested, the dog and I take off on a
dead run to the River, diving head first into the deep

place where currents cut down to cold artesian water,
breath catching as my face splits the surface like the prow
of a ship—taking me to places even ships can't go.

John Milisenda, *Viviane*, detail of photograph

Postcard

Before I knocked, Ricky's mother
     would open the front door and continue
sewing in the family room while I
     made it into their kitchen and lowered
my empty bucket under the running faucet
     in one effortless grunt.
                    And then I'd be out again,
balancing the water weight on my ankle-
     bone as I cut through the shared lawn,
shaking over the spikelets and spilling nothing.
     In our kitchen I'd dip empty Tupperware
into the borrowed water and turn the vertical blinds
     so the stalks of light would fill the brims with a broth
of similar light. While mom slept off her hunger,
     dreaming we'd die and be plotted in the tile,
I sifted the morsels of stucco-ceiling reflected
     bowl by bowl along the breakfast table.
                         Yes,
     we rose one morning, vacated the house, surged
through the lawn and upturned bicycles
     spinning wind in the driveway—yes.
If you ask me now, I'll tell you
     the leaves on our trees were a hundred
jazz hands, the sun a cow, or a moon,
     depending on the day, the time, the tendered
sashay of this earth.

Northern Lights

There was no stopping you
even after the green card came.
You still took the local section to bed
& flipped to the migrant stories,
every article yours
to consider: If you, too, were shot
in the head on your way
across the border, would you
bleed a bullet & five nights,
then set a signal of fresh grass
on fire? Someone else did.

It's another night & again
you can't tell a star
from an ember, so you follow both,

trailing the pulse of a song
sung along the palms. Somewhere
you're seeing that first band of smog
refracted, the blued headlights, oncoming,
the mile ahead, the blanched road
& its dividing bones driving you.

Separation

At eleven in the morning, darkness fell.
My son reached for my hand, but I was gone.
Like a sun-starved plant gone stringy

and bare, he struggled after that.
Strata of buried homework hidden
beneath books and backpack,

and a hollow spot within,
like the sunken circle in the yard
where once the elm tree rose.

In the newspaper: a mother
snuggles her children in their seats
before rolling the car into a lake.

Children can live under the water.
When they emerge on the far shore,
you cannot take your eyes off them.

One night I found him in the kitchen,
his muscular chest and skinny legs
covered in long underwear.

He was writing a song called "Eating
Mr. Hoover." At Mass next morning,
he pocketed the Eucharist.

The wafer of bread, the body of Christ
rested in the dark tomb of his pocket,
as if awaiting resurrection.

Each day I check the mailbox
for a small blue envelope, a soldier's
letter, words full of the distance

between Minnesota and Iraq.

He tells me stories of himself,
without the ending.

I can hear their rustling wings
at the door. When I open it,
long, feathered necks crane,

talons claw at his ID, his sad,
hard face. But there is no hand
to reach for or touch.

How to Make a Knife in Prison

The rec yard brims
with 219 shades
of brown & Sam leans
like a stolen hubcap
against a bend
in the fence. He works
a section over,
pushes and pulls
at a curve until a ten-
inch slat falls
like afterbirth in his
palms. To onlookers
distance turns his slight
fingers into fine
manicured digits
as he tucks the slender slab
near his crotch. Sam
starts a circuit around
the quarter-mile track
in his mind chasing silhouettes
of ex-lovers, his nostrils
clouded with the sweat
of men. Lockdown

brings him to his knees.
His hand grips
the scrap like a priest
about to carve
a God. He sprinkles
water near his feet
to keep the blade
from folding, slides
its edge across
concrete. Sam hunches
into his nine-year-
old self, nudging
ants with the broad

end of a wiffle
bat. The hands
remember this,
as he works
that piece
of fence into
enough.

Manly Johnson, photograph

why not lazarus?

Swann Rd cast an umbra over the regal down-tilt
      of the Yankees-fitted Brandon sported. The flint

of brothers who careened down dusky alleys
      darkened the glint of his eyes and the ammonia

stink of luv hit the air like bad wine when he dug
      into the pocket of his fatigues. We called it boat:

the black of marijuana wet with embalming fluid.
      Brandon outstretched in the bed of a crimson pickup,

its owner asleep in one of the small apartments
      that circled Brandon's body like smoke rings.

When smacked his eyes danced, a copper nickel
      spinning on a table as he pulled the open end

of a Garcia Vega unwound and re-rolled with yellow-
      blackish poison fattening its brown skin. Any soul

within ten feet would inhale the carcass of a slow possum
      crawling into his lungs. His lips now the tracings of autumn

colors: soft brown, to mahogany to the black once pink
      of edges that would grip a blunt until it burned shorter

than a nubbed pinky nail. We watched the thwap
      and gurgle of JYB's wink on the congas pour life

into his stilled body. Drenched ourselves in rumors
      of what a bad batch of ill could do; how it bequeathed

a three-day high and nudged Brandon's head to lilt
      over the percussion as he stripped naked and ran with ghosts.

Stillness No. 4

It is always a vicious proposition, forgetting everything else,
the blank page and whatever music happens to be playing.
Working up to the point of release—there is the initial tightening,
a constriction of conceit, as I have said before. Though I didn't mean it,
nor know what it meant. I can always remove the optimism,
inflate moroseness. The eager motions never cease. Most
are turquoise remnants and a tar-flavored song—a wild make-over
toward sadness. But that isn't it. You know. That isn't it. Exactly.
The Barbie doll behind the stove. Her hair is dirty.
Khrushchev and Nixon wash one another's clothes.
Behind the washing machine, a streak of blue paint
swashed to the side of this statue, the paragon of images
and symbols. What is a television for? The boy plays with dolls.
A better definition for progress. Wielding. Where was I?
This turns on a moment. Turns back and sees in the street, a child.
The child takes hold of the cars and bangs them together. Puddles form.
Passing by, plastic brown shoes crack and turn into passion.
They walk past puddles. Cracked becomes artist. A thinner streak
this time, white obscures the pavement. Paint over the clitoris
and paint over the penis. Candy canes, we've made up baboons,
scared the elephants, spit on donkeys, you make the chime
from rusted cans—allow a fortunate dream to subsist and permit
the breath of life. She blinks. Home. You there.
You beside the lion's cage, with jean jacket proclivity, take her
to her dream world, if you dare—stand up to the universe
then and there, lead Barbie by her dirty hair and feed her to the lions,
again. One cloud moves. One cloud moves, the same cloud moves,
it is a gray cloud. Paint now, with a soft brush, sunlight.

Self Portrait as Democritus

Rembrandt van Rijn, oil on canvas, 1669

Here in the year of his death, he's done himself
in the rough tone of The Slaughtered Ox, a cheerful geezer,
his toothless mirth dissolving into the white noise

that saturates this black canvas—he'll not die of it,
this laughter, but he's fading under his glowing cap.
There's a figure, a bust, behind him, so he's in

his studio tarnishing himself, what better word?
the plague has taken Titus to a rented grave—
Time's running out—nothing cuts like an old saw—

Democritus is said to have put out his eyes
in order that he might avoid outside disturbance,
not such a cheerful way to guard his thoughts—

better, perhaps, to draw the curtain, welcome
the dark from which a few more images may spill,
among them the joke for which there is no laughter,

fit for this laughter, for which there is no joke.

Portrait of Jan Six

Rembrandt van Rijn, oil on canvas —1654

Here the gentleman has come into our room.
His scarlet cloak hangs from his shoulder,
and he's willing it to stay in place, a shrug

that brooks no uncertainty — see (because
the painting holds him still) how the business
of his hands, one bare, tugging at the gloved other,

is like a flushing bird, wings working only echoes
of the rough brush strokes — his face is stern,
both serious and still like the moon rising

over the black (why is our room so dark?)
which moves just as this sentence through
pigeon-gray, the coat; ocher, the chamois gloves;

and that hanging cloak, drenched scarlet.
He's come in from the lighted world and he'll take
in a moment, from this darkness, our hands.

Subway

This morning the subway's nearly empty but
an ancient woman inside a mountain of rags
squats by the tracks shouting curses

at voices in her head, or us, or the dead, who
can tell. We're still careful after yesterday's stupid
squabble ended with lovemaking like paper

boats struggling against undertow. Just up the tracks
a dreadlocked guy intones a two-chord
autobiography, guitar case open for cash, while

an opera poster for *Aïda* salutes his tragic
composition. A few silent graybeards in black
overcoats line concrete benches waiting as if

for news of rain or some other
reason to go on. The train's late, but no one
besides us is going anywhere. You next to me,

head pointed away, but your body heat
pulses to mine. What will I do on the day
that you board one train, and I

another? Love, even when this crooked
heart shall vanish, my ashes will shimmer,
singing the alphabet of your name.

Take Bitter for Sweet

Each poem a stranger shanghais us sleep
drunk into a rickshaw rattling through this small

town dawn—incongruous
and alone with only our own strangeness

for company. Yes, and under a sea of stars, we fall
backward into our lives, from water

into water. I, half-witted insomniac, outside
in my robe at first light, attempt any negligible

truth, but, as usual, I'm not
equal to the task. Bleary, I stumble

into the honeysuckle bush whose silver leaves
cup orange and crimson berries. I measure

the weight of fruit in my hands, each
destiny held by nothing. Call it gravity, chance,

or family dynamics by whose impeccable
vertigo we navigate constellations drawn

from a game of pick-up sticks. Still,
the dust of the world is everywhere, luminous

in this air I'm breathing while, upstairs in our bed
softly snoring, your unhappiness

blossoms over our pillows, its runnels
whispering my helplessness. All I have

to offer is a handful of saffron, plus a few
liquid notes from the finches shacking up in our

neglected apple tree. I say neglected but
what I mean is, left to wildness and the love

I will surely die of. If every poem's a stranger,
then this dark form leans

against ghost light while a rickety
travois clattering

down an unlit street spills the loose
beads of my need

for you. The paperboy tosses today's bad
news at the neighbor's porch, as I

mingle my breath with yours, same
world, same cast of fools and angels

taking bitter for sweet. Isaiah the prophet
preached, *Woe to those who mistake*

gall for honey, day
for night, but my tongue

fills with brine and rose, apple
and ash when I say life's

hard enough — let us make of it
what we can. This exile

calls you home.

YEMI AGANGA, a Nigerian-born citizen of Botswana, has lived in South Africa, the United States, Lesotho, and Botswana. A poet and slam artist, he has been featured in Ishmael Reed's *Konch* magazine as well as the publication *English in Africa* and *Word Riot* online literary journal. He and St. Lucian-born Canadian poet Yannick Marshall will release a debut collection of poetry, *Old Friend We Made This For You*, this year.

MEENA ALEXANDER was born in India, raised there and in Sudan. Her first poems were published in Sudan, in Arabic translation. She teaches in the MFA program at Hunter College and the PhD Program at the Graduate Center. Alexander has published several volumes of poetry, including *River and Bridge*; two novels *Nampally Road* and *Manhattan Music*; a collection of both prose and poetry, *The Shock of Arrival: Reflections on Postcolonial Experience*; and her autobiography, *Fault Lines*.

J. MAE BARIZO was the winner of New School University's Year of the Writing award. In 2006 she was a finalist for the Joy Harjo Award. In 2007 she received an International Publication Award from *Atlanta Review*. As a prize-winner in the William Stafford Award, she was published in *Rosebud*. Her work has also appeared in the *Baltimore Review*, *Sink Review*, *Poetry Motel*, and *Antietam Review*. Ms. Barizo is also a professional musician. Born in Toronto, she lives in New York City.

DANIEL BECKER practices and teaches internal medicine at the University of Virginia School of Medicine. He graduated from the MFA program in writing at Warren Wilson College in 2004. He also builds wooden boats.

ELVIRA BENNET is an archivist living north of Boston. She has published fiction and poems in a variety of journals and an essay called "Kafka and Girls."

REGINALD DWAYNE BETTS writes poems and runs a book club, Young-MenRead, for children in the DC Metro Area. His work has appeared or is forthcoming in *Gulf Coast*, *Crab Orchard Review*, *Obsidian III*, *Poet Lore*, and *Hanging Loose*; he is currently at work on a memoir, *A Question of Freedom*.

MICHELLE BITTING has work forthcoming or published in *Glimmer Train*, *Prairie Schooner*, *Crab Orchard Review*, *Passages North*, *The Comstock Review*, *Many Mountains Moving*, *Rattle*, and other journals, as well as a chapbook, *Blue Laws*. She has won the *Glimmer Train* and *Rock & Sling* poetry competitions. Recently, Thomas Lux chose her full-length manuscript, *Good Friday Kiss*, as the winner of the DeNovo First Book Award.

IAIN BRITTON's poetry is published internationally. His work has recently appeared in *Heat, Jacket, Otoliths* (Australia), *Vallum* (Canada), and *Agenda* (UK). Work is forthcoming in *Ambit, Envoi, Stand, The Warwick Review* (UK), *Harvard Review, Bateau Press, Poetry Salzburg Review,* and *The Continental Review* (Europe).

LARSEN BOWKER is an English teacher and university tennis coach. His work has appeared in *Poet Lore, Connecticut Review, The Midwest Quarterly,* and many other journals.

MICHAEL CAMPAGNOLI won the *New Letters* Poetry Award in 2001 and the All Nations Press Chapbook Award in 2004. His fiction and poetry have appeared in *Stirring, New Letters, New York Stories, Saint Ann's Review, Illuminations, Southern Humanities Review,* and elsewhere. A chapbook, *Ah-meddy-ga,* was published in August 2005, while a second chapbook is forthcoming in 2008. Three of his poems have been nominated for a Pushcart Prize.

BARBARA SIEGEL CARLSON has recent work in *River Oak Review, Hunger Mountain, Metamorphosis,* and *Natural Bridge.* A collection of the poetry of Srecko Kosovel (co-translated with Ana Jelnikar) is due out from Ugly Duckling Presse in 2009. Carlson translated the poems in this issue at The Golden Boat International Poetry Translation Workshop held in Skocjan, Slovenia, in 2006. She lives in Carver, MA.

HAN-HUA CHANG represented hospital workers in Local 1199 for twelve years. Next year he will be the Upper School Educational Integrationist at the Calhoun School in New York. He has published in the *Potomac Review, AmerAsia Journal* and *Nimrod.*

MARY P. CHATFIELD's poems have been published in *The Atlanta Review, California Quarterly, The Wisconsin Review, Persephone, Literary Imagination, The South Carolina Review,* and *Meridian Anthology of Contemporary Poetry,* among others. Her translation of the poems of Pietro Bembo was published in 2005 by Harvard University Press, as part the I Tatti Renaissance Series. She is currently at work translating the poetry of Cristoforo Landino for another volume for the series.

CRAIG COTTER was born in 1960 in New York and has lived in California since 1986. His first full-length collection, *Chopstix Numbers,* is available from Boise State University's Ahsahta Press.

ANNE CROSSMAN is co-author of *Getting the Most out of College: A Professor, a Dean, and a Student Tell You How to Maximize Your Experience* (2008). Her poems have been published most recently in *Margie: The American Journal of Poetry* and now *Nimrod*, and she has written over two dozen children's stories produced by Little Fox Publishing Company. She currently lives with her husband and sons in Seattle, WA.

PRIMOŽ ČUČNIK's first book of poems *Two Winters* was awarded the Best First Collection Award. He has published a number of poetry collections since: *Rhythm in Hands*, *Chords*, *New Windows*, and his *Selected Poems*. He writes literary criticism and book reviews, and works as an editor for the literary journal *Literatura*, as well as runs a small publishing press, Sherpa. He lives in Ljubljana, Slovenia.

HEIDI CZERWIEC is assistant professor of Literature and Creative Writing at the University of North Dakota, where she is the Co-Director of the annual UND Writers Conference. She has written two manuscripts of poetry, *Cleave* and *Dead Metaphor*. She has poems and translations published or forthcoming in *Hunger Mountain, California Quarterly, Valparaiso Poetry Review, Smartish Pace, Barrow Street, The Greensboro Review, Quarterly West, Western Humanities Review,* and *Hayden's Ferry Review*.

CHRISTINA WOŚ DONNELLY has lived on two rivers, the Niagara and the Potomac. She is a founding co-editor of *Not Just Air* and the author of a chapbook, *Venus Afflicted: Poems 1999-2002*. Her work has appeared in print and Internet publications such as *Lilliput Review, Slipstream, Stirring* and *The 2River View* and six anthologies, most recently *Susan B & Me*.

CHRISTOPHE LAMIOT ENOS has published two collections of essays, *Water on Water* and *Hospital Literature!*, as well as three poetry collections *Apples and Oranges, Sitôt Elke,* and *Traveling Toward Tenderness*. He lives in Paris.

CJ EVANS's poetry has recently appeared or is forthcoming in journals such as *American Letters & Commentary, Chelsea, Court Green, Cincinnati Review, LIT, Mid-American Review,* and *Washington Square*. He lives in New York City.

ELYSE FENTON has most recently published work in *Natural Bridge, The Massachusetts Review,* and *Meridian*'s *Best New Poets 2007*. She lives with her husband in Austin, Texas, where she works as a writing instructor and a farmhand.

KATE FETHERSTON's poems and essays have appeared in numerous journals, including *Third Coast, Artful Dodge, Hunger Mountain, Interpoezia,* and *Poetry Miscellany*. She co-edited *Open Book: Essays from the Postgraduate Writers' Conference* (2007) and *Manthology: Poems on the Male Experience*

(2006). Recipient of a 2004 Vermont Arts Council Individual Artist's Grant in Poetry, she is at work on her first collection of poems.

MARIA FIRE began seriously writing and submitting poetry at fifty. Along with her prose and poetry memoir, *Knit One, Haiku Too*, she has published poems with literary journals across the country. She and her husband live in the mountains of Asheville, NC, and have two grown sons.

LESLEIGH FORSYTH has had poems published in *The Sarah Lawrence Review, Big City Lit, Lumina,* and *Rattapallax* and has work upcoming in *The Westchester Review*. She is an active amateur cellist and runs a lecture series in Larchmont, NY, where she lives with her husband. She has two grown sons.

KATHARINE GREGG has been an editor and teacher—of English to 8th- and 9th-graders—and is now a part-time marketing director for a small publisher called Hobblebush Books in Brookline, NH. She lives in Mason, NH, surrounded by gardens and cats.

TERRY HERTZLER's poetry and short stories have appeared in a variety of publications, including *The Writer, North American Review, Margie,* and *Stand Up Poetry: An Expanded Anthology*, as well as being produced on stage and for radio and television. He is the owner and publisher of Caernarvon Press, a founder of the San Diego Writers Cooperative, and coordinates the monthly Second Sunday at Open Door Books poetry series in Pacific Beach, CA, now in its fourth year. His latest book of poetry is *Second Skin*.

MARCIA L. HURLOW's first full-length book, *Anomie*, was a winner of the *Edges* prize. Her work has appeared or is forthcoming in *Iodine Poetry Journal, Cincinnati Poetry Review, Confrontation*, and other publications.

MICHAEL JOHNSON was born in Bella Coola, British Columbia, and lives in Vancouver. His work has appeared or is forthcoming in *Weber Studies,* the *Pedestal Magazine, Malahat Review,* and *Southern Review*, among others. He'd be deliriously happy playing cricket for a living.

JANINE JOSEPH was born in the Philippines, and now lives in both California and New York. Her work has appeared in or is forthcoming from *Salt Hill, Fugue, Askew, Caribbean Writing Today, Bear Flag Republic: California Prose Poems and Poetics,* and *Homage to Vallejo*.

NEIL GABRIEL KOZLOWICZ worked in Kalamazoo as dishwasher, prep cook, and roofer while completing his degree in English, which led to an

MFA at the University of Minnesota. He now bakes bagels and provides web services for authors in Tucson, where he lives with his wife, daughter, and two dogs. The poem "Stillness No. 4" is from his manuscript collection *An Evening in Tube Arts*.

SUSAN LANDGRAF has spent four months teaching at Jiao Tong University in Shanghai this year; this is her second trip to China. She has been awarded a writing residency at Footpaths in the Azores and on the island of Flores will work on a nonfiction book about "the new modern China in its old, old tradition." Her chapbook, *Other Voices*, has been accepted by Finishing Line Press. Her latest poems for 2008 appear in *Poet Lore*, *Rattle*, and *Pontoon*.

LORI LEVY's poems have appeared in *Lullwater Review*, *Portland Review*, *Rattle*, *MacGuffin*, *International Poetry Review*, and a variety of other literary journals. Born in New Jersey, she grew up in Vermont, lived in Israel for sixteen years, and now lives in Los Angeles. She is married and has three young adult children.

KELLY LUCE's work appears in *The Gettysburg Review*, *Fourteen Hills*, *The Cafe Review*, and *Alimentum: The Literature of Food* and online at *Common Ties* and *Review Americana*. She was a finalist for the *Indiana Review*'s Fiction Prize in 2006. Originally from Chicago, she now lives in the Santa Cruz mountains.

MYRNA AMELIA MESA is an MFA degree candidate at Old Dominion University. Two of her poems won first place in the 2008 Old Dominion University College Poetry Prize sponsored by the Poetry Society of Virginia and the Academy of American Poets; two others were Finalists for the 2007 Rita Dove Poetry Prize, and one a runner-up for the 2008 Poetry Contest of *Columbia: A Journal of Arts and Literature*. She is currently completing a collection of poetry on her Afro-Cuban ancestry.

PAUL MIHAS teaches creative writing through the continuing education departments of Duke University and the University of North Carolina at Chapel Hill. His work has appeared or is forthcoming in *Pindeldyboz*, *Talking River*, *Harrington Gay Men's Literary Quarterly*, and *Northwoods Anthology*. He lives in Durham, NC, and is currently working on a collection of stories based on recent travel to China, Argentina, and Greece.

TERESA MILBRODT received her MFA in Creative Writing and her MA in American Culture Studies from Bowling Green State University in Ohio. Her stories have appeared in *North American Review*, *Crazyhorse*, *The Cream City Review*, *Hayden's Ferry Review*, *Sycamore Review*, and *Passages North*,

among other literary magazines. Her work has also been nominated for a
Pushcart Prize.

ANESA MILLER, a native of Wichita, KS, holds a PhD in Russian language
and literature from the University of Kansas. After teaching for 12 years,
she is now enrolled in the MFA program at the University of Idaho. Her
poems have appeared in *Texas Review*, *Iris*, *The Spoon River Poetry Review*,
and other journals.

IRIS MILLER is a visual artist, an art teacher of city children, and an art
therapist. Her work has appeared or is forthcoming in *The Sow's Ear Poetry
Review*, *miller's pond*, and *The South Carolina Review*.

ANN MINOFF graduated from New York University with a degree in
philosophy and continued her education at the National College of Chiropractic in Illinois; she received her Doctorate of Chiropractic in 1982.
She currently teaches yoga and offers classes on Kabbalah. Her work has
been published in *The Literary Review* and *Porcupine*.

CAITLIN NEWCOMER lives in Columbus, OH, with her partner and their
beloved cat. She currently holds a University Fellowship at The Ohio
State University, where she recently received an honorable mention for
the 2007 Academy of American Poets Award.

JUDE NUTTER was born North Yorkshire, England, and grew up in north-
ern Germany. Her poems have appeared in numerous journals, and she
is the recipient of several awards and grants. Her first book-length collection, *Pictures of the Afterlife*, was published in 2002. *The Curator of Silence*,
her second collection, won the Ernest Sandeen Prize from the University
of Notre Dame and was awarded the 2007 Minnesota Book Award in
Poetry. A third collection, *I Wish I Had A Heart Like Yours, Walt Whitman*,
is forthcoming. She currently works in Minneapolis.

MARGARET OKERE received her MFA in Creative Writing from Pennsylvania State University. Her poems have appeared in the *North American
Review*, *Calyx*, *Taproot Literary Review*, *Mobius*, *Avocet*, and *Poe Talk*. She
currently teaches at Pennsylvania State University.

GAIL PECK's first chapbook won the North Carolina Harperprints Award,
and her first full-length volume won the *Texas Review* Breakthrough
Contest. She has published two chapbooks, *Foreshadow* and *From Terezin*,
and a full-length volume, *Thirst*. Her work has appeared in *The Southern
Review*, *The Greensboro Review*, *Rattle*, *Brevity*, *Cave Wall*, and elsewhere. She
was a finalist for *Nimrod's* 2007 Pablo Neruda Prize for Poetry.

GERI RADASCI has been a journalist in Chicago and Connecticut, an English teacher, a corporate communication specialist, and now a freelance writer. Her publications include her latest book, *Tightrope Walker* (2007), *Trapped in Amber* (2005), and her prize-winning chapbook, *Ancient Music* (2000).

THAILA RAMANUJAM won first prize for the Short Fiction Award given by the Bookshop Santa Cruz, and she has been a finalist for the Glimmer Train Press competitions. Her work has appeared in *Readers* and been anthologized by Kalachuvada Literary Publications in India.

MICHAEL SHAY was born in Germany, studied at the University of Iowa, and makes his living as a commercial photographer in Portland, OR. His profession supports his avocations of writing poetry and making even more pictures.

JEFF SIMPSON is a student at Oklahoma State University, where he is pursuing a master's degree in creative writing and works as an editorial assistant for the *Cimarron Review*. His poems have appeared or are forthcoming in *H_NGM_N*, *Gulf Stream*, *Big Muddy*, *Poet Lore*, *Nimrod*, and *Pebble Lake Review*.

STEPHANIE SOILEAU's short stories have appeared in *Gulf Coast*, *StoryQuarterly*, *Tin House*, and *New Stories from the South, Best of the South: From the Second Decade of New Stories from the South*. She is a graduate of the Iowa Writers' Workshop and is currently a Wallace Stegner Fellow at Stanford University, where she is working on a collection of stories and a novel about fishermen, oil and erosion in coastal Louisiana.

ANNE STAMESHKIN recently earned her MFA in fiction from the University of Michigan. A freelance writer and editor, she lives in Brooklyn and is working on a novel. "Carried Away" is her first published story.

LORI STOLTZ published a chapbook of poems, *Sleepers in the Wake*, in 2001. She has been poetry editor for *Water-Stone Review* and sub-editor, writing and editing for Ashdown Publishing in the UK, and teaches English, at Rochester Community and Technical College and Minnesota School of Business, among other schools.

CHAD SWEENEY is coeditor of *Parthenon West Review* and the author of *An Architecture* and *Arranging the Blaze*. Chosen for *Best American Poetry 2008* by Charles Wright, Sweeney's work has appeared in *New American Writing*, *Barrow Street*, *Crazyhorse*, *Black Warrior*, *Poetry International*, *Colorado Review*, *Runes*, *Denver Quarterly*, *American Letters & Commentary*, and elsewhere. He is a PhD candidate in literature/poetry at Western Michigan University in Kalamazoo, where he lives with his wife, poet Jennifer K. Sweeney.

CHRISTIAN TERESI's poems and interviews have recently appeared in *The American Poetry Review*, *The Notre Dame Review*, *The South Carolina Review*, and *The Writer's Chronicle*. He is the Associate Director of Membership for AWP and lives in Fairfax, Virginia.

DANIEL THOMAS is completing an MFA at Seattle Pacific University. He has been most recently published in *The Bitter Oleander* and *Poetry Ireland Review*. He works in the PBS system as Chief Operating Officer of Twin Cities Public Television in Minneapolis.

ANDREA THORSEN received her MFA in Poetry from Washington University in St. Louis. She currently lives in St. Louis, Missouri.

LI C. TIEN, born in China, is a retired PhD engineer in Midland, Michigan. He has patented a sunlight-info dial and published papers in mathematics. His poems have appeared in *Green Hills Literary Lantern*, *Poet Lore* and other journals. Classical Chinese poems translated by him and John Palen are in *Blue Unicorn* and *Renditions*.

LENORE WEISS's most recent collection is *Sh'ma Yis'rael*. Other recent publications include *Bridges: A Jewish Feminist Journal* and *Women in Judaism*. She has published three chapbooks, *Public and Other Spaces*, *Come Untogether*, and *Business Plan*. Her CD, *The CellPhone Poems*, explores changing boundaries between public and private space. She is currently working on a collection of "tkhine," modeled on 17-century Yiddish prayers by Jewish women.

CHARLES WYATT is the author of two collections of short stories and a novella: *Listening to Mozart* (1995), *Falling Stones: the Spirit Autobiography of S.M. Jones* (2002), and *Swan of Tuonela* (2006). His work has appeared recently or is forthcoming in *Beloit Poetry Journal*, *Artful Dodge*, *Sonora Review*, and *Barrow Street*. His poetry chapbook, *A Girl Sleeping*, won the 2006 *Sow's Ear Poetry Review* contest and was published in 2007. He teaches creative writing and literature at Denison University.

ANTHONY DOERR, judge of the 2008 Katherine Anne Porter Prize for Fiction, is the author of three books, *The Shell Collector*, *About Grace*, and *Four Seasons in Rome*. Doerr's short fiction has won three O. Henry Prizes and has been anthologized in *The Best American Short Stories*, *The Anchor Book of New American Short Stories*, and *The Scribner Anthology of Contemporary Fiction*. He has won the Barnes & Noble Discover Prize, the Rome Prize, and the Ohioana Book Award twice. His books have been selected as a *New York Times* Notable Book, an American Library Association Book of the Year, a Book of the Year in the *Washington Post*, and a finalist for the PEN USA fiction award. In 2007, the British literary magazine *Granta* placed him on its list of 21 Best Young American novelists. He currently teaches in the MFA program at Warren Wilson College. From 2007 to 2010, he will be the Writer-in-Residence for the State of Idaho.

MARK DOTY, judge of the 2008 Pablo Neruda Prize for Poetry, is the author of eight books of poems, among them *Fire to Fire: New and Selected Poems*, *School of the Arts*, *Source*, and *My Alexandria*. He has also published four volumes of nonfiction prose: *Still Life with Oysters and Lemon*, *Heaven's Coast*, *Firebird*, and *Dog Years*, which was a *New York Times* bestseller in 2007. Doty's poems have appeared in many magazines including *The Atlantic Monthly*, *Ploughshares*, *Poetry*, and *The New Yorker*. Doty has received the National Book Critics Circle Award, the *Los Angeles Times* Book Prize, a Whiting Writers Award, two Lambda Literary Awards and the PEN/Martha Albrand Award for First Nonfiction. He is the only American poet to have received the T.S. Eliot Prize in the UK. He is the John and Rebecca Moores Professor in the graduate program at the University of Houston.

ABOUT THE ARTISTS

SARAH ATLEE was born in Norman, OK, and grew up in Albuquerque, NM. In 2007 she was chosen as one of seven Oklahoma artists to participate in the first Art 365 project sponsored by the Oklahoma Visual Arts Coalition. This exhibition, which includes Sarah's series titled "Normal, OK," opened in Oklahoma City in March 2008.

JOHANNA BURTON is a painter whose work involves fabrics and printmaking. She recently completed her MFA at The University of Tulsa.

GLENN HERBERT DAVIS is an Assistant Professor of Art at The University of Tulsa. He was the recipient of a Oklahoma Visual Art Fellowship in

2006. His work has been exhibited and published nationally, with his most recent solo work, "image of one," exhibited at Berry College.

SHANE FERNANDEZ is an architect living in Tulsa, OK.

JUAN FRANCO, photographer, is a native of Colombia. He has explored and photographed all over the world, especially South America.

JORDAN HALDANE is a student at Edison High School in Tulsa. The photograph in this issue was part of the Telling My Story Project, funded by the Kennedy Center for the Arts.

JEFFREY HOGUE is an artist living in Bartlesville, OK. He is represented in Tulsa by Joseph Gierek Fine Art.

JOHN MILISENDA's photography has appeared in over 125 shows and publications including *Smithsonian* and the *New York Times*. His work is in the permanent collections of the New Orleans Museum of Art, the Museum of Modern Art, and the Bibliothèque Nationale.

CORRY PARKER is a student at Edison High School in Tulsa. The photograph in this issue was part of the Telling My Story Project, funded by the Kennedy Center for the Arts.

DARSHAN PHILLIPS is a co-founder of Live4This, which operates as a collaborative multi-disciplinary design and art studio. As artists, art directors, advertisers, designers, and photographers, Live4This explores the overlap of fine art and commercial design.

I.C. RAPOPORT began his career in photojournalism with *Paris-Match Magazine*. His many *Match* photos include pictures of John F. Kennedy, Fidel Castro, Marilyn Monroe, Samuel Beckett, and Eva Gabor, among dozens of other icons of the time. Rapoport has also been published in *Life Magazine*, *Time*, *Sports Illustrated*, and *National Geographic*. Rapoport now lives in Pacific Palisades, CA, and Manhattan, and is currently a film and television writer.

JORG SCHMEISSER is an internationally recognized artist and teacher of printmaking. He moved to Australia in 1978 to direct the printmaking workshop at the Canberra School of Art.

Nimrod International Journal

The *Nimrod* Literary Awards
Founded by Ruth G. Hardman
The Katherine Anne Porter Prize for Fiction
& *The Pablo Neruda Prize for Poetry*

First Prize: $2,000   Second Prize: $1,000

Postmark Deadline: April 30 of each year

No previously published works or works accepted for publication elsewhere. Author's name must not appear on the manuscript. Include a cover sheet containing major title and subtitles, author's name, full address, phone & email address. "Contest Entry" should be clearly indicated on both the outer envelope and the cover sheet. Manuscripts will not be returned. Entrants must have a US address by October of each year. Work must be in English or translated into English by the original author. *Nimrod* retains the right to publish any submission. Include SASE for results. The results will also be posted on *Nimrod*'s Web site in June: www.utulsa.edu/nimrod. Poetry: 3-10 pages. Fiction: one short story, no more than 7,500 words.

Entry Fee: Each entry must be accompanied by a $20 fee. $20 includes both entry fee & a one-year subscription (2 issues).

- -

To subscribe to *Nimrod*:
Please fill out this form and send it with your check.

$18.50 for 1 year, 2 issues (outside USA, $20)
$32 for 2 years, 4 issues (outside USA, $38)

Name _____

Address _____

City_____ State _____ ZIP _____

Country_____

For more information, to submit, and to subscribe:
Nimrod Literary Awards
The University of Tulsa, 800 S. Tucker Dr., Tulsa, OK 74104
918-631-3080   nimrod@utulsa.edu   www.utulsa.edu/nimrod

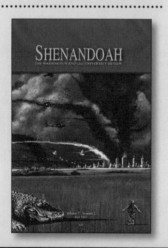